THE CONSCRIPT D

The Conscript Doctors

Memories of National Service

~

Compiled and edited by
JOHN S.G. BLAIR

The Pentland Press Limited
Edinburgh · Cambridge · Durham · USA

© John S.G. Blair 2001

First published in 2001 by
The Pentland Press Ltd.
1 Hutton Close
South Church
Bishop Auckland
Durham

British Library Cataloguing in Publication Data.
A catalogue record for this book is available
from the British Library.

ISBN 1 85821 946 9

Typeset by George Wishart & Associates, Whitley Bay.
Printed and bound by Antony Rowe Ltd., Chippenham.

Contents

Foreword vii

Author's Note ix

Introduction xvii

Chapter I   The National Service Era 1

Chapter II   The Home Base 13

Chapter III   Trains, Planes and Ships 40

Chapter IV   The Western Theatre and the British Army
of the Rhine 52

Chapter V   Around the Mediterranean 72

Chapter VI   The Suez Venture, Aden 91

Chapter VII   Africa 106

Chapter VIII   Malaya 131

Chapter IX   Hong Kong 150

Chapter X   Korea 158

Chapter XI   Special Assignments 176

National Service Medical Officers' Archive 199

Foreword

John Blair has a flair for telling a story – in this case many stories within a story – through the mind's eye of those newly qualified doctors compulsorily conscripted for two years after the Second World War to all three Services, not forgetting students who graduated in medicine after doing their national service in 'other ranks'.

Except for those born into the Services, or into a coal mining family in the case of those arbitrarily selected by numbers to work in the pits, the experience invariably involved a traumatic and disorienting adjustment, especially for the newly married and those given perverse postings – as was only too common. However, the contributors to this compilation seem to have benefited from their experiences in every corner of the world, although some had to make the best of unremitting routine duties. They also seem to have resisted the temptation to become alcoholics and inveterate smokers.

An obvious question is whether the experiences of our conscripted colleagues, revealing as they are, anticipated their future careers. The evidence, albeit from a largely self-selected sample and with the advantage of hindsight, is encouraging. This miscellany abounds in examples of young doctors who were to scale the apex of their chosen specialties, taking or making opportunities to enhance their experience and to develop heightened confidence. One such was our current leading clinical scientist who was carpeted, but mercifully not cashiered, for publishing – without permission from the War Office – a paper on thalassaemia which he had diagnosed in a Gurkha child whose illness had baffled the entire medical might of the RAMC. Conversely, there was the leading pathologist of the future who achieved the lowest mark in his intake's IQ test, which must be presumed to have been flawed.

The belief that sporting prowess was an advantage is also fully vindicated. The compiler himself – no mean golfer – was the hero of an historic match.

For lovers of the telling anecdote, the book is studded with gems: delicious gaffes such as passing an open snuff box around the table at a Mess dinner; the hilarious dinner on board a battle ship in the midst of an horrendous storm during the Suez campaign whilst swaying 30° either side of the upright; the explanation for the early fatal crashes of the technologically advanced Comet aircraft due to decompression explosions; the gripping account of a nuclear test on Christmas Island witnessed from a presumed safe distance by a medical officer who registered a higher geiger counter reading than the operational air crew, due to the thorium in his Swiss Omega wristwatch; the M.O. called in by the Army Dog School in Germany to condemn meat because the dogs were not allowed to be fed food fit for human consumption.

There is also a darker side to the picture, exemplified by the distinguished future public health physician who oversaw the elimination of the usual infectious diseases on his patch only to see them return as soon as the country concerned became independent. There is also sad evidence of petty corruption, vindictiveness and incompetence which the national servicemen, unlike the Regulars, were not prepared to countenance, although they were obviously limited in their ability to rectify such situations.

To quote from the final chapter: 'The national servicemen held the fort for 15 important years . . . they swelled the ranks of our Armed Forces at a time when our nation . . . could not otherwise have provided the numbers needed to garrison the West, deter the East, and support emergent countries worldwide.'

Our conscript colleagues have done more than that. They have provided rich veins of sepia-tinted reminiscence which will be mined both by those who, in retrospect, can be seen as privileged to have served in the Defence Medical Services, and those who have not. Their testimony echoes down the tunnels of time and casts revealing light upon countries which later generations of visitors explore as mere tourists.

Sir Alexander Macara

Author's Note

IT IS NOW 40 YEARS since the end of National Service. The National Service Era is unique in British history as the only period when there was conscription in peace time. All young men were called up for two years' full-time service, followed by a spell in the Reserves. Almost everyone did National Service, the only exceptions being those who had an illness or disability, and a very few who contrived to evade their commitment for selfish ends. All of us remember some of those with contempt. A record of the experiences, reminiscences, and memoirs of those doctors – newly qualified on call-up – and from all three Services – seemed something unique to collect. I approached BMA and the Wellcome Institute for the History of Medicine, and was given immediate support. Professor Vivian Nutton of the Wellcome Institute, and Mr Richard Smith and Sir Alexander Macara of BMA, were particularly helpful. The Wellcome Trust gave me a generous research grant, which I acknowledge with thanks. Help was given *via* 'Minerva's page of the BMJ.

This is a powerful collection. Much of the material is of such value that it would have been a tragedy had it been lost. Wellcome, because they are supporting the archive, have stated that all material accepted will be kept in perpetuity by them, and that it will be protected until twenty years after the contributor's death. This has allowed former NS officers to write as they wish, with criticism where they feel this is necessary. It has also made the material very much more lively, entertaining, and illuminating.

Most of us then realized how lucky we were, having missed the war, and so we were content to serve. But, and especially as the decade of the 1950s passed, more and more young doctors were angry at 'the waste of two years' National Service, and became antagonistic.

Because of this, a significant number of those approached have failed to provide a reminiscence; a few have actively refused. Those who have written their recollections may then represent only one side of National Service – the others have simply not contributed. From personal knowledge, I am aware that those working in large training depots were the least happy. This pattern applied not only to the Army, but also to the other two Services.

By contrast, Regimental Medical Officers (RMOs) with units enjoyed the camaraderie of the Regimental spirit, and many memoirs are full of praise and admiration for their Regiment or Corps. They had active training exercises, especially overseas. In the RAF, the majority were in home stations – although many reached as interesting overseas postings as in the Army – but they shared the interest of the flying squadrons, and the pride that went with them. In the Royal Navy, service at sea was just what an enthusiast in the Navy looked forward to.

Postings to hospitals overseas, and to the then world-wide spread of the British Empire, opened a new and exciting life. When you grew up during the War there was no foreign travel. In many instances you did not even move far from your own home. Not only was there now the novelty of the ship travel to the Middle and Far East, but on arrival there was the fascination of a foreign country. Different disease was a reality. Some parts – Korea and Malaya, but also Trieste and Aden, had active shooting warfare in progress. Real casualties occurred and had to be evacuated and treated. Because they were given huge responsibility abroad, which a newly-qualified doctor would never get at home, many felt their National Service had given their career a permanent direction and boost that would never have occurred otherwise. This comes out over and over again in the written records.

This collection has several elements worth recording in book form. First is the fact of conscription and the military service it involved from basic training onwards. These are military history. The account of the 1st Argyll and Sutherland Highlanders in Korea, by Douglas Haldane, is outstanding.

This battalion, with the Middlesex Regiment the first British infantry units committed at the harsh start of the Korean war, had as many casualties during its first three months as its sister battalion suffered in its corresponding period in the Crimea. The Middlesex Regiment too shared this bad period. William Lewis Owen tells the story from the Naval side – his ship sailed along the coast of Korea prepared to 'do a Dunkirk' if our side were beaten back to the sea by the North Korean army. His account is yet another unique one.

Active operations in Malaya, during the Communist inspired revolt, and in Aden and Trieste, are well covered. In the National Service period, from 1948 onwards, the Cold War was much more of a reality than it became twenty and thirty years later, when the Soviet threat was seen as something delivered by rockets or by submarines. The early tension is seen in the records from the British Army of the Rhine and from Berlin.

The worth and variety of the medical clinical and public health memoirs themselves make the archive fascinating, even if no other aspects had been included. It was not only in Malaya and Hong Kong that medical disease and its management was recorded, and not only by two of several famous names – Sir David Weatherall and Sir Roy Calne – but by a wide range of men who in later years became noteworthy in all aspects of medicine. It must be remembered that the entire graduate output of British medical schools went into the Forces in NS times and so the entire range of talents went with them. Another, whose Malayan experience set his whole subsequent career on its course, was Hughie Webb, first Professor of Neurovirology at St Thomas' Hospital in London. Africa, from the Canal Zone in Egypt to Libya, Nigeria, the Sudan, Cameroons and Kenya, are covered by a range of doctors of high quality who later became physicians or neurologists or bacteriologists. Some memoirs came from the Caribbean and Central America. A few are of general practice among the families of servicemen, with all the problems that included.

But perhaps the most fascinating part of the whole archive is its worth as social history. On the way to his posting, the young man's troopship tales are full of zest, and at times, scandal. As Captain Iain Stewart put it: 'The troopship romance stuff was probably Mills and Boon or Barbara Cartland – as far as I could observe – but who knows. Troopships had a reputation for unleashing suppressed passion and desire among the travelling females . . .'

Postings, and their apparent irrationality, are commented on again and again. Lieutenant Andrew Graham, a Glasgow graduate, became friendly with John Smith, a London graduate, on their troopship to Egypt. When they arrived in the Canal Zone, Graham found himself posted to the Staffords as their RMO, Smith to the Highland Light Infantry. Neither could understand a word his patients were saying! An initial posting order requiring special instruction in tropical diseases was changed at the last moment to one to Wales or north Germany.

On arrival at the unit, the attitude of the NS towards their seniors in the Regular Services, non-medical as well as medical, will be another source of research surprise and amusement in fifty or a hundred years. One later highly distinguished professor's stories of his various wrong forms of evening wear at dinners on his troopship to the East is pure P.G. Wodehouse. The dismissive attitude of the senior Regular to the NS is well told by John Heber – and others. (John Heber was a Guy's graduate, interested in anaesthetics. When in Malaya, he devised a neat, small, portable anaesthetic apparatus. 'Splendid, Heber,' said his CO, 'you can test it in the jungle.' 'But the jungle's full of terrorists, Sir,' was John's reply. 'Excellent, Heber,' quipped back the colonel, 'I see you read your intelligence briefings.')

Sport naturally was a common source of activity, and several were posted to a place where the Service could make the most of a skill. Rugby, hockey, boxing, athletics and golf are all featured. The tie match in the Army Golf Championship at Royal St Georges in 1954, and the seven o'clock play-off, with senior officers having had a good number of drinks accompanying each match, went into the mythology of that sport for many years.

Social life was full of spice. Drinking and smoking were commonplace – often to excess. Dr Ross Coles, later an ENT surgeon, remembers, on joining the Navy in 1953: 'When I was first interviewed by the Captain, a man eventually to become a full admiral, he asked us three new officers whether we smoked. I did, but the other two did not. "Well, I expect all my officers to smoke.

And the two of you who don't, you damn well learn to. When we entertain, you carry cigarette case and a lighter and you offer cigarettes to our guests and smoke one yourself to keep them company." A direct order from a superior officer – to be disobeyed at your peril.'

The life of spice the young wives of Regular officers on route to join their spouses had on troopships has been alluded to. NS of course were never allowed to have their wives with them, or if they did, had to pay all travel, accommodation and rent. Comments of a few wives of National Service doctors are in the archive, with their views on their welcome, or lack of welcome, by Regular Service society.

Large numbers of virile young men living in often sparse conditions far from home meant that their sexual appetites had to be satisfied locally. In the Far East, and also in Germany, there were also plenty of girls equally happy to slake this desire. Sometime a tense situation arose. An MO on leave from Korea in Tokyo had a Japanese girl in a hotel bedroom. Hearing American Military Police were about to search the hotel, he put his small lover inside his greatcoat and hung them both inside his wardrobe! She was not discovered.

There are also poignant anecdotes. Dr John Grant recalled a doctor in his own intake who was posted to a large military garrison in the south of England. He was allotted his room in the mess, and on his first evening, chummed up with a pleasant quiet medical officer in the next room – he looked in to borrow a match. They became firm friends, and shared the rest of their two years together. Some years later, his friend confided that he had been so unhappy that he had been going to shoot himself, and would have done so the next day had the new doctor not appeared on the scene and restored his spirit.

RAF memories have their special interest. They, too, contain some hilarious recollections. But they also include accounts of those involved in important military research – one describing the Atomic tests at Christmas Island, another of the development at the Royal Aircraft Establishment in Farnborough.

The second smallest number are from the Royal Naval Service.

The rather different emphasis – National Service Officers were described as RNVR and badged accordingly – although not volunteers – is well shown. That these NS men enjoyed their period of full-time service is evident by the number who became active and enthusiastic members of the RNR afterwards.

There is a last, smallest group, of those who did conscription in another way. Dr John Scott, later a consultant psychiatrist, telling of his time as a miner, Dr Anthony Dixon, OBE, telling of his active service with the British Red Cross in the Far East, and Dr James Macgregor, OBE, of his in Sierra Leone as a Colonial Medical Service doctor, and later in the Solomon Islands, make up this group.

At the end of their two years, or during their service, many National Servicemen were given a range of inducements to sign on for Regular commissions. The best story of all these came from Captain Brian Ashworth, whose Commanding Officer told him in Kaduna: 'Ashworth, you could finish up a brigadier if you stayed in.' 'But I don't want to finish up as a brigadier, Sir,' replied Brian. He became a consultant neurologist in the Royal Infirmary of Edinburgh.

I have written this short account of the recollections of the conscript doctors from the United Kingdom of Great Britain and Northern Ireland in the National Service Era at the request of the British Medical Association and Wellcome, in order to make known the wishes of a very large number of the contributors, that their memoirs are recorded not in a closed archive, but in book form. I thank them each and every one very sincerely for the time and trouble they went to, in producing records of the highest standard. Their age as described belongs to a half century ago; national characteristics of loyalty, patriotism, *caritas*, were present then without doubt, and disrespect, narrow nationalism, the need for finding scapegoats and the constant urge for litigation, were absent. Sad events and accidents were overcome without 'counselling' by eager enthusiasts, and those involved recovered quicker with comrade compassion. There is much, of course, not recorded here. That makes up the *real* magic of the memoirs. But the public will have to wait a further half-century before these become available.

In the meantime, we who shared the National Service experience will have many a good laugh as we have our memories stirred. We hope others will share our enjoyment too.

Introduction

Air Marshal Sir John Baird KBE DL MBChB FRCPE FRCSE FFOM FRAeS DavMed

Surgeon General, United Kingdom Defence Medical Services, 1997-2000

O VER THE CENTURIES, conscription of men into the armed forces in time of war has been a common practice in this and other countries. Indeed in its most brutal form 'press-ganging' sailors into the Royal Navy was an early example of obtaining service from men who were not volunteers. There are of course always men (and women now) who volunteer for service in the armed forces and make this a full career. Peacetime conscription might seem an anomaly. Why should any country require large numbers of non-volunteer sailors, soldiers and airmen when there is no immediate threat to national security? In an ideal world this should not be necessary, but of course it is not an ideal world and there may be many lesser threats or commitments falling short of all-out war which need more servicemen than can be supplied by volunteers alone. The present world situation provides many examples of just such scenarios which are stretching our armed forces at this time.

Many countries resorted to peacetime conscription – and several still do – but the United Kingdom only did so between 1948 and 1962. This book tells the story of the National Service years as they affected doctors. Most young men were conscripted immediately after leaving school but because the Services were desperately short of medical officers it was necessary to defer medical students' call-up until after they had qualified. They then fulfilled their National Service obligations as young medical officers and provided a crucial role in the Services in those days of hugely expanded numbers of servicemen. The United Kingdom was one of the first countries to revert to all-volunteer Services and the last doctors began their National Service in 1960 – ending in 1962. The all-volunteer status pertains to this day, but the shortage of medical officers in the Services is more critical now than it has ever been.

The era of National Service came to me second hand. I was one of the 'deferred medical students' in 1955 and conscription ended before I had qualified. I was one of the few medical officers in the early sixties who 'signed on' voluntarily – and I have to say with no subsequent regrets at all! My knowledge of National Service for doctors was anecdotal, both from doctors back in the NHS when I was a medical student and later from older colleagues in the Services who had started as National Servicemen but who had enjoyed the life so much that they converted to short or full commissions. This is one of the intriguing aspects of National Service. It seems that most (not only doctors) did not wish to serve, hated the concept and their involvement at the time, but in retrospect they look back on their two years as hugely rewarding, satisfying and character-forming! Obviously some did not and regarded their time as a conscript with loathing and as a total waste of time. This is sad when one hears of the good times others had. Many National Service doctors went on to very prestigious civilian careers and some of them have contributed to this collection of memories.

I have read the book with great interest and nostalgia (for something I never experienced – but my early 'regular' years were very similar!). I was fascinated to find anecdotes and stories from medical men I knew, some very well, told with great humour and with a reluctant fondness for the good old (bad old?) days! John Blair is a renowned and consummate medical historian and he has collated a memorable selection of stories. He must take huge credit for his research in identifying, tracking-down, and coaxing the contributors to put pen to paper. The result is a marvellous account by those who took part in this significant time in our history. It has already been referred to as 'one of the most important collections of medical historical material of the twentieth century'. Because it came just after World War Two the National Service era has often been sidelined – but it should not have been. I should like to think that this book will go a little way to redress the balance and at last will give recognition to all the medical officers who did so much for their country in a time of need.

CHAPTER I

The National Service Era, 1948-1962

THERE IS MUCH in the background to know about before we can really understand the story of the doctors who were conscripted for National Service between 1948 and 1961. It was indeed a unique period in the whole of British history, when there was conscription during peacetime, and the doctors were among the thousands who were involved. Their Era, the National Service Era, merits recording in the history of our country and of the three Services involved – the Army, by far the largest, the Royal Air Force, second in numbers, and the Royal Navy, smallest in number but as important as the other two.

It included a critical time for the transition of the RAMC and the medical branches of the RAF and RN, when the changes of the new National Health Service and its new requirements for medical training had to be appreciated, and their implications understood. For the most part, these were handled well.

As a social study the National Service Era is of immense interest. Apart from a very few who did not do National Service, either from physical inability at one end of the spectrum to selfish contrivance at the other, the whole of the young male population of Britain entered the Armed Forces over a fifteen year period. That this unheard-of novelty succeeded was in large measure due to the resilience and cheerful tolerance of the British tribes – English, Welsh, Scots, and most Northern Irish, when the young and their parents were recovering from the exhaustion of a World War. Two historical aspects, of significance when the concept of military call-up outwith war was proposed, may be discussed first.

The first was what may be called the soil – the feelings and attitude of the boys and youths themselves, and their parents. The second was the seed – the passage through parliament of the necessary legislation.

It is nowadays totally forgotten just how exhausted the British were by the end of 1945. They had sold almost all of their overseas financial wealth to keep the war effort going. The children and adults who were in the home base had suffered bombing, and had learned the meaning of the blackout, clothes and food rationing, so that those of us in that age range have never got over the feeling that we must always leave a clean plate. Rationing would continue until the mid-fifties, industry would be slow to pick up in spite of the efforts of the post-war Labour government. It was the tiredness of a nation which had held the ring for a century, and by the inexorable law of history, was about to feel that retirement had much to commend it.

Bombing of the UK base had made everyone tired. Over 66,000 civilians had been killed. For the first time, fear *for* near relatives was a factor in the breakdown of servicemen all over the world. The appearance of the V1 and V2 rockets to the south in 1944, when all thought that major raids were over, produced large casualties. The V2 was the first Scud missile, which I can remember myself clearly as an explosion out of nowhere. Fortunately it had no chemical component. But the threat of gas was real. All of us remembered gas drill from the first days of the war in September 1939. And behind it all now, by 1945, was the huge threat of the atomic bomb.

Everything just described made the youth tired and thin. Many had lost a father or older brother, in the Forces; mother or sister in the bombing by the Luftwaffe. A returned Prisoner of War from the Far East – where the rations could not have been called substantial – said when he saw his younger brother of 17 years: 'Gosh, isn't the boy thin!' Like their elders, the food-rationed young wanted real peace and they wanted it badly.

Now we can consider the general and particular political background. Mobilization of the Territorial Army and Regular Reserves had been set in motion by the Reserve and Auxiliary Forces Act of 25th May, 1939, 2 and 3 George VI. 'Whereas a situation has arisen in which it is necessary that His Majesty should be empowered, whenever the service of his reserve and auxiliary Forces is urgently required for ensuring preparedness for the defence of the realm against any external danger; to call out for service such of them as may be needed: Now, therefore, be it enacted by the King's most Excellent Majesty, by and with the advice of the Lords Spiritual and Temporal, and Commons, in this present Parliament assembled, and by the authority of the same . . .'

The detailed provisions of the Act, couched also in terms which remind us that continuity is one of the greatest assets our small nation possesses, followed. The original Act was to last for three years in the first instance, but if 'an address is presented to His Majesty by each House of Parliament praying that this Act should be continued in force for a further period of one year from the time at which it would otherwise expire, His Majesty may by Order in Council direct that this Act shall continue in force for that further period.'

This particular Act was for the Territorials and reservists of the world, who had volunteered and contracted for call-up under the very conditions expressed – by King's proclamation. Later in the 1939-45 War, conscription was ordered, as always by Act of Parliament, for those who had not so volunteered. Conscription would last until the end of hostilities, and then it ended.

While the end of the Second World War brought to an end the threat of German domination – at least for a time until its resurgence at the beginning of the next century – it quickly became apparent that the move of the Soviets west was posing the biggest threat to western Europe since the days of Charlemagne, when the Saracens were at their most militant. Their western boundary extended to the Eastern Zone of divided Germany. All the eastern European countries were subject. The Poles, for whom Britain and France had gone to war in 1939, were now prisoners of the Russians. Berlin was an isolated island within – the Berlin airlift, another of the Battle Honours of the RAF, saved the city from incorporation.

Soviets had almost reached Denmark and the North Sea, but were foiled by Allied intervention. Their Communist creed, however, made no secret of its intention to take over the corrupt world of the west. 'We will bury you,' said Mr Kruschev.

In all parts of the world its agents were at work. Oxford and Cambridge, always hotbeds of revolutionary causes, had their open cells and traitors already secretly in post. They would not be exposed until many years later. In the Far East, Communism was the victor in China, where the later horrors of the cultural revolution were also to become public in due course. Communists were active in Australia. The march of Communism was irreversible, its proponents declared. Many western socialists were sympathetic.

The new world order was called by Mr Winston Churchill 'The Cold War', and its continuance over the next forty years would determine all military strategy during that time. Fears were most immediate in Europe and in Malaya, where Chinese guerrillas looked likely to take over the peninsula and beyond. Open warfare would soon break out in Korea.

It was all this which led to the unique period in British history, when conscription would be called for in time of peace and would last for fifteen years. One army would be needed to go to Germany as more than a mere post-war garrison; it would have to guard the eastern boundary against the Soviet bloc. In the Far East, active operations would also require many troops; the errors of 1941 dared not be repeated.

And so, in 1945, it was clear that a further Act, to be called a National Service Act, had to come before Parliament. The Labour Government, voted into office by a huge majority, was expected by some to sweep away all traditional institutions. But it did not, and was composed of true patriots who had the nation's interests at heart. The patriotism of a number, however, did not rate the Armed Forces a high priority.

Mr Attlee, the Prime Minister, posed the difficulties on 4th March, 1946. He noted the need to allow demobilization and release of those who had served in the War – only, as he said, seven or eight months back – but not at the expense of destroying the efficiency of the Forces. He noted the burden of the occupying Forces needed in Austria, Italy, the Far East, Greece, Palestine, Java, and Persia, as well as Germany. He was aware of instability in a way perhaps not acknowledged by government at present.

'I want to deal with a matter on which I know there is some criticism. While our commitments remain as they are, we must continue to call up young men for the Services. The complaint is that we have not yet decided on the length of that service in future. I am aware of the difficulties for the young, their parents, educational establishments.'

When the Army estimates were debated in 1947, Dr Haden Guest referred to the Medical Services in words which have a late twentieth century ring about them. He spoke of the 'acute difficulties of medical manpower in the service of the nation.' He went on: 'if the Services are to function properly, they must have a complete, skilled medical service. That is an inescapable obligation. We have also to remember that the National Health Service is beginning in 1948 and will make great claims. We have to balance the two. Specialists in particular are in short supply, and there is no good professional training available.' He saw clearly the small size of the training base and the difficulties this would pose.

Dr Guest had gone around military medical establishments and found poor communication between junior officers and their commanders. The working party of members of Parliament who had visited with him also found that the response to recruiting was poor. Less than half the numbers required – and this was for all arms – were coming forward.

By 1947, the National Service Act was to be brought before Parliament. 'Be it enacted . . .' The preamble was followed by the meat of the Bill.

1 (1) Subject to the provisions of the National Service Acts, 1939 to 1946, and this Act, (which Acts are hereinafter referred to as the National Service Act) every British subject who has attained the age of 18 years and has not attained the age of 26 years and is ordinarily resident in Great Britain shall, by virtue of this Act, be liable to be called upon to serve in the Armed Forces of the Crown for two terms of service, that is to say:

a) a term of whole-time service, that is to say, service in the regular Forces for a period of twelve months or such shorter period as His Majesty may by order in Council appoint, and

b) a term of part-time service as defined by this Act . . . which was in effect to be six years following the last day of his whole-time service. During that time, the reservist was to undergo up to 21 days in any year or 60 days in the whole period of his part-time service.

Perhaps the most significant point in the whole of this Act is the statement that service was to be in the Regular Service, that is to say, the man was in effect a one year regular soldier, sailor or airman. He was not in any way different, as far as how and where he must serve, from his regular comrades. National Servicemen could call themselves, therefore, Regulars on a limited term. National Servicemen were to serve anywhere in the world, with any Army unit or HM ship or RAF station, including units normally open only to volunteers, like paratroopers or submariners.

I believe this concept is correct, even though only once previously expressed, and gives a clue to the relationship between National Service and longer term Regular which we will examine later. But when the Bill came forward for formal reading, it was a 2-year period which was deemed essential, and not a 1-year, said Mr A.V. Alexander, the Minister. The longer term at once produced antagonism, and the debates in the early part of 1947 are worth reading. The opposition became such that the Government offered to reduce the term to 18 months.

Next, with the enthusiastic backing of the Liberal Party, the Bill's opponents tabled an amendment to reduce the term to 12 months. Later again, as well as the left-wing Labour members, who opposed the Bill on idealistic as well as political and economic grounds, the Liberals wanted it thrown out altogether. Mr Clement Davies, the Liberal leader, said the Bill infringed the personal liberty of the people. 'The Liberal Party,' he said, 'remained true to their convictions . . . would anyone in Moscow be influenced that our young men were being conscripted? This is a challenge I will fight to the end.'

Mr Davies went on to remind the Labour Party of their taunts against Mr Neville Chamberlain in 1938 when he sought to introduce a Conscription Bill. 'They accused him of going back on his pledge to the people.' How little if ever do politicians change.

Among the many speakers in the debates of April 1947, two are worth quoting. Mr James Callaghan, newly elected member for Cardiff South, made strong attacks on the attitude of the Labour Government to the Armed Forces. 'We cannot maintain these huge forces that we have today. We cannot continue them for a second longer, and they should be drastically cut. There are greater risks in not reducing our Armed Forces than in reducing them.' He went on to insist that the Soviet Union would never have it in mind to attack the West.

Mr R.A. Butler, of the Conservative Opposition, reminded the government of the need to maintain the Regular element. 'The intricacies of modern war,' he said, 'and the complication of weapons, demands a core of long-term professional soldiers.'

At the division, 242 Labour members voted for the Bill, the 131 rump of Conservatives, 8 Liberal Nationalists, and 7 Independents. 72 Labour MPs, all 10 Liberals, 2 Independent Labour and the 1 Communist, voted against. Mr Price White, a Welsh member, said he voted against because no-one in Wales would have conscription. On the other hand, the Northern Ireland members pleaded for their young men to be included.

The outcome, then, was that the National Service Act, with a 2-year term at that, would arrive on the Statute Book. After their 2 years with the Colours, they had five years of Reserve service, during which time they could be recalled.

From the start of 1948, National Service became an accepted fact of life for all young men leaving school, and from the three medical branches of the three Services, for all young men going through Medicine. The Regulars would have an influx of talent and variety equivalent to that in time of war. For undergraduates, all those liable knew that failure for a second time in a Professional Degree Examination meant instant call-up as a sailor, soldier or airman to a basic training unit. The initial numbers included those who had just missed the War – some had been in wartime Home Guard units – and those who had had compulsory training in the university Senior Training Corps (STC) as undergraduates. Very many non-university schoolboys had been in the Army Cadet Force, and Boarding Schools had Junior Training Corps.

Those who had STC training – and that was all students initially – knew well the rigours of basic infantry training, since the tough 'battle training' introduced in 1942-43 had not lightened in the years 1944-45. This meant that they were conversant with the lot of the squaddie in the many and large training depots where all Arms and Services substituted National Servicemen for war-time recruits.

The training was similar; the only difference was that the recruit was being trained for a two year peace-time career and not for posting to a fighting unit at the end of his six weeks. Alongside the National Service majority were the minority who had engaged into the long-term Navy, Army, or Air Force for twenty years. This was not quite true, however, in many instances. If the Service unit the recruit was entering was somewhere on active service, those passing out would go to a war theatre – and as we shall soon see, the Regimental Medical Officer posted to that unit or ship was on active service also.

Where would he go? The British Army of the National Service Era was large. There were still over one million in 1948, and even five years later, half a million. Training depots were abundant all over the United Kingdom, particularly in the big garrisons of Aldershot, Catterick, Tidworth and Salisbury Plain, Colchester, Chester, where the the men were drilled on the same square the Romans had used, and London. For the Royal Navy, there were Portsmouth and Plymouth, for the Royal Air Force, Lytham and Halton. Because of the very large needs of the NS Army, war-time camps such as Blandford, Ripon, Lichfield, Barnard Castle, Oswestry, Rhyl, Barton Stacey, Hindhead and Yeovil were retained – none of which had been such large military areas before in peacetime.

The British Armed Forces were deployed all over the world. They made up forces of occupation in Germany, Austria, and Japan. RAF squadrons were deployed wherever the Army was. In 1948 internal strife with serious security problems in India, Palestine, and the Far East, and on the borders of Germany and Yugoslavia, needed an operational level of troops. And the Navy still had its ships world-wide, but especially in the Mediterranean and the Indian Ocean and Singapore.

By 1949, although Britain had withdrawn from India, Ceylon and Burma following the granting of independence, and from Palestine following the setting up of the State of Israel, there were still garrisons in Malta, Cyprus, Aden, Egypt, Hong Kong, the West Indies, and in East and West Africa. The Trieste British element remained. Active warfare was taking place in Malaya and there was a real shooting war in Korea. There were units of Army and Air Force in France, Belgium, Holland, Eritrea, Cyrenaica, Tripolitania, and Somaliland. The British Three Services were dispersed, in fact, more widely than they had ever been.All these garrisons and stations required medical cover in varying degree.

During his last clinical year the medical student received his call-up notification. Because of the size of the Army relative to the other two Services, this was for the RAMC unless he had made a positive request otherwise. There was no selection for the RAMC as there was for the Royal Navy, and Army pre-service interviews were uncommon.

After medical qualification there was a medical examination, carried out as a rule by general practitioners at the town's local recruiting board (which at times struggled with the newly devised PULHEEMS system of Service medical classification), or, in a garrison town, at a Regular medical board. These were moderately strict examinations, including a chest X-ray. The grossly overworked housemen of those days often turned up exhausted on their half-day, and were told by their examiners that their health would soon improve with the open air activity for which His Majesty's Forces were so famous.

The actual call-up date was not strictly determined. Since there were two intakes a month, officer entry could be delayed to suit an examination, or for family reasons. The largest intakes of medical officers were in July and August, corresponding to graduation dates, or in March at the end of the first house job. In the first years of National Service there were no pre-registration posts – a graduate in medicine at a British university was under no legal or moral obligation to do one until 1953.

RAMC had by far the largest number – from some 20 minimum to 80 at the twice-yearly graduation periods. RAF varied from about 7 to 20, and RN were again smaller.

A small minority were able to delay their call-up for longer than one year – if they obtained a junior registrar's post (equivalent to today's senior house officer). The extra experience, if long enough, or sometimes the higher qualification passed ahead of the field, gained them clinical status above the ordinary general duties medical officer (GDMO). In the RAMC, GDMO was the lowest level. Such had just to take whatever posting was given. The one above was 'GDMO with experience' – usually meaning up to six months of extra training or say the DRCOG, the Diploma in Obstetrics of the Royal College of Obstetricians and Gynaecologists. The other group which had the chance of a better-than-average-place to go, was made up of those who had special ability at a sport. Some of these were posted to a site in the south of England and represented their shore establishment, RAMC, or RAF Station week by week.

The stage above was 'clinical officer', awarded to those who had an extra year of post-graduate training. The two highest levels, junior or senior specialist, needed more time than the incoming NS officer would normally have, but a very few attained this level. Extra training was encouraged, for example, for anaesthetists or laboratory specialists, since the Regulars had nowhere the numbers required to meet the needs of the big Services of the day. A very few brightly academic young doctors thus found themselves advising their seniors on the newer advances in the fields of bacteriology, pathology, or biochemistry. The same applied to obstetricians and anaesthetists in an anaesthetic department in Malaya or the Canal Zone, or in a small maternity unit in Benghazi or Tripoli or East or West Africa.

Except for those whose real disability or illness barred them from serving, or those, not forgotten for the rest of their lives by their classmates, who deliberately avoided serving, the notice of call-up always arrived. Armed with this legal document, requiring upon pain of severe punishment our reporting at a clearly stated date and place, and enclosing a railway warrant for a third class ticket to that military destination, we set off. RAMC went to Crookham near Aldershot for basic military instruction, in three parts, military first, including how to behave at formal occasions, then to London for instruction in military pathology, and finally back to Keogh Barracks for a week each in the Army School of Health and the Field Training School.

RAF prospective medical officers went to Lytham St Annes, where, as Eric Mackay laughed, 'It was carefully hidden away – for you never saw such drill.' Like others, he found the commanding officer of the basic training unit less than impressive. 'Ours was a disappointment. We felt he had allowed his soul to desiccate and really had little of the doctor left in him. He attempted to introduce us to the mystery of a "dining-in night". When well in his cups he demonstrated his party-piece *extraordinaire* by painting a face round his navel and altering its expressions by contraction of his abdominal musculature. It was not a pretty sight, not helped by ours being a mixed company. The ladies however had a suitable riposte. The next day when our over-hung CO was attempting to marshal us into a semblance of a "passing out parade", the two ladies drove onto the parade square after proceedings had been under way for some minutes, parked the car on the "sacred" ground and joined the ranks in a most un-military manner. He almost died, but consciously decided it were better to let us go – pronto! – and said nothing.'

It was Portsmouth for the Senior Service, where cutlass drill was added. Ross Coles remembered: 'My naval uniform had two straight gold stripes on each sleeve, the upper stripe bearing a square ring above it, the insignia of the Royal Naval Volunteer Reserve (RNVR). For such as I to be described as a volunteer was puzzling since we were conscripts, but I was soon to learn that life in the Services was full of anomalies. The rank given to National Service medical officers was curious too – Temporary Acting Surgeon Lieutenant, RNVR. What a mouthful! Temporary meant two years full time and Acting meant we were really sub-lieutenants, but as most of us would have been aged about 25 on entry and had an honours degree or equivalent, perhaps two stripes were felt to be more appropriate.' As far as cutlass drill was concerned, he added: 'Cutlass drill is normally done with double spacing to make sure that the next man is out of cutlass reach as it is waved about in the various drills, but for medical officers they were more prudent and had triple spacing.'

Nearly all of us were commissioned on call-up, but a number subsequently graduated after doing National Service other ranks. Alec Leete and Dr Geoffrey Seddon (who as a private RAMC turned down the chance of a posting to the Far East so that he could prepare to become a medical student) in the Army, Dr K.G.R. Somer, Professor Robert Blueglass – later Consultant Psychiatrist to the RAF, and Professor Barry Jackson – later President of the Royal

College of Surgeons of England – in the RAF, told their story of recruit training from the squaddie's point of view and then of being medical orderlies for two years. What happened to us after we all arrived at our place of initial posting will make the rest of this story.

CHAPTER II

The Home Base

THE LARGEST NUMBER of malcontents among the National Servicemen was amongst those who put in their time within the UK. This was inevitable when the job was in a large training depot, often within a huge garrison, and consisted of processing several hundreds of recruit entries every fortnight. Not only were there the repetitive medical examinations and inoculations and vaccinations concerned with the process for two solid years, but there were the inevitable breakdowns of all sorts, physical and mental, always commonest during the first six weeks of recruit training. Depot permanent staff were not always of the most helpful or stimulating. Complaints from parents went to Members of Parliament, and the Government of the day were not by any means sympathetic to the doctor, 'a young and untrained National Serviceman whose work was not always able to be supervised' as one famous newspaper quoted.

On the other hand, those who served as RMO to a Regiment, or were in an active RAF station, or who had been fortunate to be posted to an Army or RAF hospital where their work was interesting, which it was not always – enjoyed a much happier two years.

One other group was in a category of their own – the sportsmen, who were carefully posted to a home unit because they were good enough at a sport to be members of their particular Service's team. At Crookham, all the billet orderlies seemed to be near-professional footballers, Training Depots in all Services had Internationals in various sports on their staff, and all seemed to have ample time given for training!

In the earliest days of National Service, from 1947, the Second World War was still very recent. Dr Max White put it so well: 'The majority of recently qualified doctors was admittedly anti-service once the defeat of the Axis Powers was complete – compulsory military service seemed superfluous. We were not cognisant of the real threat from the Russian or Chinese Communist States in spite of Churchill's famous Fulton Missouri speech in 1946 describing the Iron Curtain which had suddenly divided Europe. However, the start of the Berlin airlift in July 1948 brought it home to many of us. The progressive insurgent conflagrations such as Malaya, Korea, Indian partition and then Cyprus and Suez were not even on the horizon in 1947.'

The earliest groups were called up in 1947. Max White, who was one of them, went on: 'I duly joined a group of about 40 LOPs (Lieutenants on Probation) at the hutted RAMC depot at Church Crookham, Hampshire, for our month's introductory training. The CO was Lieut-Colonel Willy Officer (that really was his surname) who confessed to us that his ethos had been moulded by his years of service to become a Regular Army officer rather than a doctor,' said Dr White. 'We were inducted into squad drill . . . many lectures did not interest us, especially those on Army organization . . . lectures on mess etiquette amused us, as we thought it so old-fashioned.'

Dr David Turk's intake of 70 in 1948 'on a wet Sunday afternoon when I said farewell to my bride of six weeks at Waterloo Station' included two ladies who had Short Service commissions. 'The training weeks at Crookham were quite good fun, particularly the endeavours of a very competent CSM to turn a rabble of 68 male and 2 female doctors into something like a squad of soldiers. In this he was hampered by the fact that one of the ladies had very short legs and couldn't keep up with us as we marched from our quarters to the barrack square; and as both ladies had shoulder-slung handbags, which couldn't be slung but interfered with the drill – so the poor CSM ended up with them slung over his shoulder, and a profound hope that the RSM wouldn't notice!

'Col W. J. Officer tried to teach us how officers should behave in and out of uniform. This and other things led to a good deal of teasing and gentle ridicule from our unruly class, but overall we learnt quite a lot that was useful and interesting . . . Just as we finished at the Depot we were invited spectators of the colonel's welcome to a batch of other rank conscripts on their first morning. Dressed in overalls, they were herded into the depot cinema/theatre – a comforting and comfortable reminder of civilian life. The proceedings began, as I remember, with the band playing the Corps march while the curtains slowly drew back to reveal the colonel standing in the middle of the stage on what looked like a large soap box with the Union Jack draped on it. After his rousing address of welcome the "finale" consisted of the band playing the National Anthem while the curtains slowly closed in front of the spot-lit colonel standing at the salute on his box. Some of us found it difficult to keep straight faces!'

At the RAMC Depot text-books were issued to the new Lieutenants. Max White was highly impressed by the tropical diseases one – 'a first-class reference book.' (*The Memoranda on Medical Diseases in Tropical and Sub-Tropical Areas*, Eighth edition, 1946, price 7/6 net if you had to buy it). He remembered 'we were asked to complete a new-fangled intelligence test designed for OCTU (Officer Cadet Training Unit) entrants – the youngest member of our intake got the highest marks, whilst the oldest, a mature pathologist, got the lowest (he was subsequently knighted after many years as a Professor of Pathology and finally as the Director of the Institute of Pathology).'

MOs posted after their initial training to training depots had similar tales to tell. The whole story of postings deserves a monograph to itself. So often, the posting given was the opposite to that asked. This will be recounted many times because it made such a lasting impression. Jack Newsom, an Edinburgh graduate of 1949, recalled: 'Because I'd done extra orthopaedics, I found myself a "clinical officer" in that. I was looking for a home posting. (Home postings were UK and Germany, at this time). At the depot, I and others went to a local pub the evening before we were due to be interviewed with a view to postings. The WOII (CSM) who took our course was in the pub. I asked him "How do I get a UK posting?" The WOII asked me why I wanted one, and I said because I wanted to do orthopaedics. He said: "No, that's no help at all." So

I said: "My wife is three months pregnant." "No," said the WOII, "That's no help at all either." He then asked me: "Do you play any games?" I said: "golf, I suppose." "What's your handicap?" asked the WOII. "18" I replied. "Well", said the WOII, "tell them you are scratch.That will guarantee you a home posting in UK." I said: "I couldn't possibly do that. They'll find out at once." But in the end it didn't matter. I got posted to the Royal Herbert Woolwich (in London) then to Hannover, lastly to Munster.'

Dr C.D.R. Pengelly was another who 'went in' from 1947. The whole of his service was done in Western Command – at Chepstow, Haverford West Military hospitals, next at Wrexham, Shrewsbury with the King's Shropshire Light Infantry, where he felt the mess was run on extravagant lines, Long Marston RE stores, and finally in the Military Wing of Baguley Hospital, Wythenshaw, Manchester. Here he had his most interesting time, as it was a Tuberculosis sanatorium and the new drugs Streptomycin and PAS were just being introduced. He saw the long, long courses of treatment which pre-antibiotic TB patients had to suffer. He saw the lines of cots containing unfortunates with spinal TB, who lay for months in plaster-of-paris shells, their sinuses being syringed out of gritty calcareous material at intervals. He saw too the men with crushed phrenic nerves, done to paralyse their diaphragms and so allow that muscle to rise and reduce the lung size, in an effort to bring about closure of the tuberculous cavities in the apices of their lungs. Lieutenant J.F. Boyd also worked in a military chest hospital, but this was the main Army one, at Hindhead in Surrey – the Connaught, as it was then called. In due time he was on the staff of the Glasgow University Department of Respiratory diseases at Ruchill Hospital. He published a monograph of note in 1961, which he sent for publication in the RAMC Journal, 'Chest Diseases in the Army' (vols 109 and 110). In 1964 he again referred to his National Service experience in The British Journal of Diseases of the Chest, in his article 'An Attempt to determine the background to Pulmonary Tuberculosis in Adolescent Males.' While at the Connaught Dr Boyd had the good fortune to meet and learn from the most famous thoracic surgeons of the day – Sir Geoffrey Todd,

Sir Clement Price Thomas, Mr Norman Barrett, and Mr Vince Powell. 'We couldn't have gained any higher education in chest medicine during our two National Service years', was his verdict.

Dr Cyril Cohen was a cheerful and able Manchester graduate who did his National Service from 1950 till 1952 'in the harsh lands of Lichfield Barracks, the HQ of the Mercian Brigade – North and South Staffordshire, Cheshire and Worchester Regiments. I shared the post of Regimental Medical Officer with Lieutenant/Captain Chivers and despite the rigours of the Midlands we lived to tell the tale.

'Emergency medicine presented situations for which I had not been trained at Medical School. One such was an urgent call in the early morning because a soldier was on his knees, with a bucket and hard brush, scrubbing the parade ground. His responses to a few pertinent questions revealed a wish to persuade the authorities that he was not fit enough mentally to stay in the army and that they would be better off if he could go home in the morning. My advice to the Duty Sergeant was that the request should be noted but that no action be taken and that in the meantime, the soldier should be allowed to continue scrubbing the parade ground – after all, it was beginning to look a bit grubby.

'I was issued with a motorized vehicle (he had learned to drive in the Army) because of duties outwith the barracks, notably to visit soldiers incarcerated in Stafford Jail. My heart sank when I was told that one of the lads threatened to go on a hunger strike. I contacted the Command Psychiatrist and he said that there was standard equipment available for tube feeding in such cases. Sure enough, there was a special box in the stores (the army had a special box for everything – quite different from the NHS!) and I signed for it. It contained what looked like a spinning top with 'rifling', a wide-bore rubber gastric tube and a page of instructions. "Place the point of the top in between the candidate's clenched teeth and gentle clockwise motion will open the jaws so that the tube can be inserted."

'I did not relish the thought of trundling up to Stafford Jail at least three times a day and so on the first visit I placed the point of the tube between the soldier's clenched teeth, rotated the instrument, inserted the tube and then repeated the manoeuvre a second time so that we both knew what we were doing. At the prospect of a third trial run the soldier indicated, quite clearly, that he wanted to abandon his hunger strike and our paths never crossed again.'

Cyril had a lovely story about overhearing a soldier telling comrades in their barrack room how to simulate an epileptic fit and so get out of the Army. 'I told him', said Cyril, 'there's a medical thing happens which a doctor knows how to test for' (he was referring to tapping the achilles tendon to produce a movement the reverse of normal, called the extensor response). The soldier came to him later, confidentially, and said: 'Captain Cohen. If you'll tell me the test I'll give you five bob.' (25p).

Royal Naval conscripts who served at home seemed to enjoy their time more. Ross Coles certainly enjoyed his time in Portland. 'In the mornings I ran the naval part of the Dockyard Surgery, which amounted to being a shore-based medical officer to the Second Training Squadron but which also allowed me to carry out some of my medical duties at sea with the Squadron during their daily training exercises. Considering the size of the Navy now (AD 2001), it is interesting to recall the size of what was just a training squadron. We had two fleet destroyers, HMS *Myngs* and *Zephyr*, and a destroyer part-converted into a frigate, HMS *Tyrian*. An old Hunt-class escort destroyer, HMS *Brocklesby*. Then there were five Castle-class frigates, HMS *Flint Castle*, *Hedingham Castle*, *Leeds Castle*, *Portchester Castle* and *Tintagel Castle*. An ocean minesweeper, HMS *Marvel* I think. My friend the anti-submarine trawler, HMS *Fetlar*, together with her sister ship, HMS *Tiree*. Finally, there was a group of four MASBs, motor anti-submarine boats which had numbers, not names.

'In the afternoons, apart from the occasional day when I was at sea I would do routine medical examinations at HMS *Osprey* . . . there was really quite a lot of work to do in that particular job, but there was also a lot of fun . . . we had an annual skittles match in Easton, but with a difference – the bowls were made of Portland stone, as were the skittles . . . at rugby, we had a curious team, United Services Portland.'

The RAF home based doctors had similar stories to tell. David Evans graduated from the Welsh National School of Medicine and managed to obtain a delay in his call-up to let him as a senior house officer attempt the MRCP examination. Sadly he failed and was about to be called up for the Army, but when he pleaded his love for aeroplanes at interview in BMA House, was switched to RAF. He entered in late 1952, went through what he called 'the rather nominal basic training course somewhere in Lancashire', then as usual went to the short Aviation Course at the Royal Aircraft Establishment in Farnborough, which he enjoyed thoroughly.

It was while at the RAE, as it was always called, that he had his very first flight in an aeroplane. Several times he applied for flying training, but the only way this was achievable was for the applicant to 'sign on' for a 5 year Short Service Commission or re-muster as General Duties. He tried again but was told firmly that the only way he could get on a 'wings course' was to take a permanent commission.

However, Flight Lieutenant Evans had many flights courtesy of 'flying types' during his two years at St Athan in South Wales. 'The sporting opportunities in the Big Service of those days were, of course, marvellous . . . While enjoying hockey, squash, etc, I concentrated on golf and won a few things including the Championship of my local club in Cardiff. Never again was I to have the time to practise sufficiently to play that demanding game at a satisfying level!

'Medically, I did little of note during those idyllic years. Because of my little bit of 'extra medicine' I was locum medical specialist from time to time . . . I was locum anaesthetist at one stage. We did a little GP. We hated 'admin'. I made some wonderful friends. The Service was my 'university of life' after a cloistered student and hospital existence.'

And he did achieve his ambition to fly. He learned while in the Royal Auxiliary Air Force, and by March of AD 2000, had flown some 4,500 hours P1 in powered aircraft and gliders.

W. G. Williams was another Welshman. He had just married in 1954 when called up. He recalled: 'There was a medical in London with a slightly mutinous group including one who brought his X-rays having broken his neck playing rugby – to no avail – subsequently upgraded to accompany the RAF expedition to the Himalayas where he was found to be an excellent climber... we reported to RAF Warton where we slept in dormitories, given uniforms, learnt the rudiments of drill (plus administration) and how to become Officers and Gentlemen. There was a distinct impression that we were there under sufferance.'

As everyone did, he found the Aviation course at the RAE full of interest. He was posted first to RAF Benson near Oxford – location of the Queen's Flight, of the RAF rowing club, and of Ferry training where all types of aircraft were flown out to the remnants of the Empire. Most of the pilots were former war-time Bomber Command and Pathfinder veterans, whose bravery he admired. 'This was a pleasant comfortable time but hardly stretched the mind especially with the social life of the mess.'

After six months, to his surprise, he was posted to RAF Hospital Nocton Hall, near Lincoln and many of the Bomber Command Airfields. Here his surgical career began.

There was one pre-condition perhaps a little different from the National Health Service. When he reported to the Commanding Officer, the CO said: 'You've come here to do surgery have you?' 'Yes Sir', Williams answered. 'Well we haven't had a Bar Officer for months. Get that in order then you can do surgery.'

He got what he was looking for – plenty of surgical work and training, in an active surgical unit run by a Regular Wing Commander, a Squadron Leader, with the rest being all NS plus one or two Short Service. Their work load included patients from the nearby Lincoln Hospital, where many conscripts who had got through the medical entry net and were found to have the usual hernias, varicose veins and other surgical conditions – exactly what the aspiring surgical trainee itched to get his hands on. Major cases were transferred to the larger hospital at RAF Wroughton. Air Vice Marshal Sir Peter Dickson, who had served during the War, acted as surgical consultant and did the more major operations.

One drawback was his and his wife's living accommodation. His wife had been a Theatre Superintendent. Her experience was naturally used and she worked in the RAF theatre, 'run by superbly trained Warrant Officer and Flight Sergeant.' However their flat in the village was miserably cold. They remembered that bitter cold above most memories! In his subsequent civilian career, he became a cardio-thoracic surgeon.

Peter Hacking had similar memories of a desperately cold home, this time in a quarter found for them while he was working at the 10-bedded MRS (Medical Reception Station) at Hildebrand Barracks near Harrogate. This served the Royal Signals Army Apprentices' School at the nearby Uniake Barracks, where the Commanding Officer was Colonel (Cool) Carne. He had won his VC commanding the Glosters in Korea.

Married and with a two-and-a-half year old daughter when called up in 1954, the Hackings were moved from furnished rooms in Harrogate into a substandard quarter in the barracks. It was a 4-roomed hut with coke fired stoves and cooker. Peter wrote in his reminiscence: 'Our second child – our elder son – was born at Harrogate General Hospital in January 1956. The bedroom of our quarter was unheated at night and I still remember breaking the ice surrounding the bottle of supplementary feed.'

They had the Matron's batman as a babysitter, 'and a very good one, too.' One morning it was noted that the quite elderly Matron was not present at the morning ward round. It was then noticed that she had not been in to breakfast. On searching her quarter, Captain Hacking found that she had been strangled by her batman and her body concealed inside a wardrobe. The batman had fled; returned, he was found to be insane. The Hackings wondered what might have been.

There was one Welshman who had a punishment posting to Willems Barracks in Wellington Lines in Aldershot. It was another RASC Training Depot. These barracks were dark, damp, forbidding. Recruits were not of the highest level. The MO there had once been MO i/c Troop Ship, holding the grandeur of temporary major's rank. This Welshman had been a man of principle who had not only refused to issue french letters (condoms) to troops when the ship berthed in Grand Harbour, Malta, but had then thrown the entire ship's supply of several hundreds into the water. He was returned forthwith to Aldershot. More than once he asked of he could live in the McGrigor Mess at the top of Gun Hill. He was refused.

Dr John Lester was particularly unfortunate in his first posting. 'I found myself sent to the Anti-aircraft Command School of Technical Instruction at Lydd in Kent and spent just under a year there. There was practically no work to do as the two units on the site (an RAOC workshop was there as well as the AACSTI) consisted of personnel who were doing reasonably satisfying and undemanding work and sick parades were small – half an hour each morning usually sufficed to deal with everything. I read diligently all the bumf which was sent me though I was amazed to get frequent reminders that you didn't use penicillin to treat malaria. What sort of doctors did they have in the regular army? I inspected latrines and cookhouses more often than seemed reasonable to pass some of the time away and inevitably got saddled with other non-medical tasks. I organized an Officers' Ball (even importing a bevy of nurses from the hospital where I had done my two house jobs) and took into my charge all the furniture and fittings of the Officers' Mess. I think they are still in my charge as I never signed them over to anyone else when I left. Going round with the Quartermaster and his inventory to check such items as "chairs, arm, officer", "drawers, chest of, oak", and the amazingly class distinctive "pokers, officer" and "pokers, soldier" gave an insight into army organization. (A "pokers, officer" was an iron rod with a knob on the end while a "pokers, soldier" was an iron bar with a loop on the end.' ('I thought you ought to know this' he added)).

Dr Martin Leadley, a Leeds graduate, gives yet another account which many will recognize. 'My National Service was the only time in my life when I was depressed', he recalled. 'Qualified in 1952, married that year, I wished to treat ill people, to support my wife financially, and to get on with my career. None of these things were possible. The Nation required my services! We could not afford or need an army of this size and my brother had died for his country in 1941. I was posted to 6 Driver Training RASC, Hounsdown Camp, Yeovil after my initial training. The only good thing about the initial training was the few weeks at Millbank next to the Tate.'

He felt he had been posted there because he was a very good footballer. Unfortunately, he seriously damaged his right ankle soon after arriving, with ligamentous damage, and was no longer able to play at a high level.

His two years were indeed a succession of repetitive tasks. He quickly found the recruit chosen to train as a NS driver was of a very poor quality, both mentally and physically. 'My eyes were opened when I saw the sort of dwarfs who were posted into the RASC. Many from Glasgow and Manchester were under the 5 feet and 100 lb requirement for training to drive a 3-ton lorry. They could not reach the steering wheel nor were strong enough to handle the heavy vehicle. Was I supposed to stretch them?' asked Lieutenant Leadley.

Intakes were 250 every fortnight. Routine went on and on, week after week. The depot staff officers tended to drink – 'It was all too easy to become alcoholic'. Also, some of the officers who had been in a 'better' Regiment and had been 'moved down', were as a result disgruntled and touchy about rank; this did not help. He did not find much in common with them.

'The high point of my two years was the birth of my first son. The low point was a day in 1955 when with three cases of poliomyelitis in the camp I was asked to address the whole lot and reassure them that all was under control. 3,000 petrified troops were drawn on the square. After one sentence, the public address system failed and my words were lost in a torrential rain storm. A wet dejected retreat ensued.'

He found that 'the way ahead in the Army was to initiate masses of paper work'. He had two trained solicitors as medical centre clerks. These two mischievously enjoyed putting together reports of all sorts of records. 'They made use of Army and legal language; it sounded good but did not make sense. But South West District and Southern Command loved them. I left the Army delighted to get on with my family life and my career.'

By contrast, Captain Martin Leadley enjoyed his short attachment to the Royal Canadian Air Force camp, where he went at the very end of his two years. The standard of officer and of accommodation there was high – he even had thoughts of doing a Short Service Commission with them.

*   *   *

RAF officers doing duty in an equivalent training camp had the same routine. James Leavesley spent his years at RAF Padgate. At Warrington, about half-way between Liverpool and Manchester, it was one of the largest of the four or five basic training camps for the RAF, and took in 350 recruits every week. Attached was a small RAF hospital which served the camp and the one or two other local RAF stations. Padgate had two medical officers, both NS, and the hospital 'boasted a Wing Commander, who was a Regular, and two more NS MOs'. The routine sick parades followed exactly the same pattern as the Army's. At 0730hrs the sick parade began, 'after the flight corporal had, with practised eye, separated the barely alive from those simulating some gross pathology (disease), (reminding them, of course, "don't forget when you visit the doctor to take your small pack, you 'orrible little man, in case you are admitted to hospital, and good riddance").' James Leavesley estimated that he had carried out 25,000 injections by the time his NS was finished! In later years, he emigrated to Western Australia, where he became a medical historian of note.

The largest Army garrison in North England was Catterick Camp, home of six or seven Royal Signals basic training regiments. There were also Armoured Regiments training centres. The BMH was in a brick and wooden hutted camp, built on Emergency Medical Service lines in the First War, with long corridors and wards leading off at right angles. It held some 500 to 600 patients, soldiers, families, maternity, psychiatry.

Dr E. J. Fairlie 'presented himself at the RAMC Depot on 1st November 1948. At the dinner that evening, it was announced that the Queen had given birth to her first son and heir.' His posting to Catterick was after only three weeks of training – as he recalled, 'the shortest period of training in the Army.' He found the camp 'in a dilapidated state', and photographs he produced certainly confirmed this description.

In 1950 Lieutenant Tony Gunn was also sent directly to Catterick from the Depot. He was at that date hoping to do surgery, a career he later followed with distinction. 'At Catterick the Accident & Emergency RSO's (Resident Surgical Officer's) room was in a noisy part, as the CO demanded the use of the (proper) RSO's accommodation for himself. You were kept awake all night', said Tony. 'I protested angrily – the CO then charged me, and I found myself before a DCM (District Court Martial) for insubordination. It came to trial – they found *against* the CO! He had said in anger: "Gunn, you will go to the Green Howards (Infantry Regiment) as a private soldier." But I went to the Green Howards as their RMO!'

Catterick was still much the same in 1954 when I was there as locum obstetrician and gynaecologist for a short spell. The long lines of hutted wards were still there. The officers' rooms were bare and cold. Each had the usual coke stove. The dentist who lived next door to me kept a large dog in his room, drank heavily so that doctors went to nearby Richmond for dental care, and the smell was hard to avoid. The Lieut-Colonel i/c Surgical Division was mostly on the garrison golf course. A flag was hoisted at the clubhouse by the professional if he was needed. If it was urgent, the pro went out on a bicycle to fetch him.

The CO was Colonel Swift. He had given in to the 90% of NS officers in that mess nights were held in civilian clothes and not in uniform. But otherwise, they followed the correct format.

In 1954 there were what seemed to be innumerable Signals Training regiments. There were also Armoured Corps Training Regiments, and we watched the cavalry subalterns hitting the sides of their scout cars with riding crops. Many years later, we happily used to go back to Catterick Garrison Course to play in the three-way RAMC golf competition for several summers on the trot. By then, in the 1970s and 1980s, there was a beautiful new BMH, the Duchess of Kent's Military Hospital.

Those with some Training Regiments had happier times. G.D. Teague, from Bristol, was called up on 5th March, 1950, after fifteen months in general practice with his wife's family doctor. Posted to the 3rd training regiment RE at Cove near Farnborough, he spent the whole of his National Service there, was granted an Army family quarter – most unusually – and even had the rent paid! His two years were 'happy though humdrum.' He shared emergency cover with the RMO of 9TRRE (Training Regiment Royal Engineers) at Southwood Camp nearby. 'The other task I was required to undertake was the judging of the Baby Show at the 3rd TRRE's annual fête at Hawley Lake which was part of the training area for the unit. I escaped unscathed.'

He was able to get early release as he had an accepted place in a university course in Public Health. The Army kept its word – in due course he was discharged early. In civilian life later he spent fifteen happy years in the TA, and later again, took Holy Orders.

Peter Merry was a great character. A heavyweight boxing Blue, his 1956 group were constantly harassed every morning by their batmen 'deliberately waking us with a fiendish din. So on our last morning I and another chap who had also played rugger for St Mary's were up in the beams of the hut with water and mud and thunder flashes, and they thought the Devil had hold of them! We were reported but the authorities were very reasonable I think in view of the fact that we had not started it. The only reasonable comment I can make is that I certainly had not realized thunderflashes are not fireworks and can cause quite severe injuries if not handled carefully.'

All the fifteen in Peter's intake had applied for an overseas posting. As ever, this was no more than a pretence – only one of them got one. Peter went to a Tank Depot in Dorset. 'There was plenty of sport and although there was only minor medicine and surgery we had a small fracture clinic and had an interesting time.'

'One of my more nerve racking incidents was caused by telling the exact truth to a senior officer. Our small hospital was being inspected by a Major General and despite all our efforts he was not happy. He fixed me with a beady eye and said if the Tank Unit was ordered to Suez could you march with them. I thought of all the P7 HO (a very low physical level, unfit for duty other than in UK) Home Only wrecks in the depot and like an ass I told the truth. I said "God Sir, we would have to carry them the last 200 miles." This did not please him and he said in an icy voice: "Do you know who I am?"

'I had however had enough. I said: "Yes, Sir, you are Major General Timber and I am Lieut Merry but I am single and very fit and think you are a fair officer. If I do my work conscientiously the only thing that is likely to happen is that I shall get posted and honestly I don't care if I get posted to the South Pole and have to sweep the snow." I expected a blast of rage but all he asked quietly was "So you are very fit are you? Do you play any games?"

'I was on solid territory now. I was RAMC hammer champion, I played second row for the Garrison rugby team, I opened the batting in the summer, and I had taken a small boxing team to the Depot. By the time I was finished all was well.'

Donald Craig joined the RAMC in 1955 after finishing two house jobs at St Thomas' Hospital. He had been at Oxford before. After the true stress (used in the way when it was not an overused meaningless word for anything the slightest upsetting) of such jobs in those far-off days, when you worked all day and all night, 'Regular nights in bed seemed a luxury, and the orientation and initiations were painless enough.'

He was posted first to a Field Ambulance at Storrington in Sussex, where a First Aid Training School was to be established. 'The idea at the time was to train officers of other arms so that they in turn could diffuse the principles down to all ranks. Along with John Webb and Glandon Thomas we devised and printed lectures from an initial position of total ignorance. We were initiates in the early days of dictating tape recorders and a unit devoted entirely to our support made an easy and pleasant Spring. We corresponded, with War Office connivance, with professors of Accident Surgery on a world-wide scale. The courses of officers changed weekly and afforded a good insight into the regular Army. Warrant officers provided Casualties Union support with mock injuries and a dramatic scenario of blazing tanks for the final examination.'

Major-General Sachs, on a visit to congratulate the staff, asked Lieutenant Craig if he would take a Short Service commission. He replied that he wanted to live with his wife in Battersea. The General then asked : 'Is there anything we can do for you?' 'Yes', replied Craig, 'post me to a fighting unit.'

'So it happened. I was sent first to the 2nd Coldstream Guards, then to the 1st Welsh Guards as their RMO in Chelsea Barracks – across the park from my wife!

'You must understand that I had nothing in common either socially, educationally, or financially with the unit, but they were unfailingly kind, accepting, and generous to me. I loved the Mess, the public duties, both in Chelsea, Buckingham Palace, St James' and the Bank, appreciated the rehearsals and the actuality of the Trooping of the Colour, and the ceremonies in general. I changed my preconceptions and understand what the Regimental System does to very ordinary men. I thought about how leadership, discipline, family tradition, and high expectation lead to intoxicating high morale and I have continued in this vein for forty subsequent years. I know that they would have rescued me, screaming in a shell hole, so that the prospect of death, and more importantly, of maiming, can only be borne when you have unarguable, unshakeable faith in your comrades. I would proudly stand on parade along with the padre on St David's Day – the only two in khaki amongst 800 in scarlet. "Who are those poor officers in khaki?" asked Prince Philip and Jill, my wife, responded appropriately.

'There were no RAMC personnel: our bandsmen were our stretcher bearers and won an Army first-aid competition. "Not less than I expected, doctor," said the laconic Commanding Officer.

'We trained at Thetford in Norfolk and I enjoyed fishing, dining in rich houses, and visiting churches. After an illicit weekend in Battersea I returned late to Thetford to find the Regiment gone and my distraught driver (Jones, who had to be distinguished from scores of other Joneses by the addition of three of his Army numbers) standing with my kit all packed in the Austin Champ. The Suez balloon had gone up without my noticing: we caught up the others near Chelmsford and the supposed toy soldiers were in deadly earnest now. After 800 inoculations and the issue of tropical clothing and painting everything sand coloured, I was marched before the Adjutant. I expected to be cashiered, imprisoned, or to have my insignia stripped from my shoulders there and then. "We have other things on our mind today doctor: dismiss."'

Very different was the hospital life. Again, some were fortunate and landed in a central, busy military hospital where the work was rewarding. David Turk applied to remain in London – he was a

Guy's graduate and his wife was in Wimbledon. To his surprise, he was sent to the central Army hospital, the Queen Alexandra Military Hospital (QAMH) at Millbank. He opted for a medical ward, and found himself 'assigned to assist the conscript Captain who was in charge of the Other Ranks' medical ward.' His superior left soon on demobilization, and he found himself in full charge. He also was awarded London lodging allowance – another bonus.

The QAMH was the Army referral hospital. The cases were of necessity often of interest and difficult to diagnose or treat. A group were under deep X-ray therapy at the next-door Westminster Hospital, used on a regular basis by the Army, for treatment of malignant conditions, especially Hodgkin's Disease. These would return for courses of irradiation as need be; many would die. He found the Regular Lieutenant-Colonel in charge 'a good physician, and the second physician was, remarkably, a Major James Dow, already a consultant physician at St George's teaching hospital quite nearby. For some reason he hadn't been called up until he was a consultant. He was promoted Major just in time to avoid the surprising designation of Lieut Dow, FRCP.' With this background, with the frequent visits by senior London consultants to the Army, Lieut Turk soon passed his own MRCP, first time. 'This was, however, something of a shock to my superiors. Regular majors who were on study leave to study for that exam at the nearby RAM College, weren't getting enough clinical experience, and used to come over and ask me, a conscript Captain, for permission to examine some of my patients. So, much though I appreciated and thanked God for my excellent job I think it was a serious error on the part of the RAMC to allow me to have it rather than one of their Regular majors.' In his subsequent career, he became a consultant microbiologist.

Sometimes a newly entered Lieutenant would be posted to the Queen Alexandra Hospital but soon transferred abroad. In 1959 Brian Pentecost, in later life to become Professor of Medicine at Birmingham and a national figure in cardiology, 'was to be the equivalent of a medical registrar there.' He too had the care of patients undergoing radiotherapy 'mostly young fellows but among them a judge who had sat at the Nuremberg trials.' He recalled examining 'recruits' for the Royal Chelsea Hospital: 'These old warriors, mostly of seventy years and beyond, lay rigidly to attention in spite of all attempts at informality. Perhaps they feared rejection by the hospital should any hint of familiarity be suspected.' His move to Germany was precipitated by a serious traffic accident involving medical and nursing staff in Munster. 'As I left for Germany I had no idea how dependent the RAMC had become on its National Service doctors.'

Captain Weisl had been posted to Malaya. Born in Prague, he had become a naturalized British subject in 1948. He completed an MD thesis in 1953 and was called up the next year. Unbelievably at Crookham, his National Service intake were not allowed to take part in a dinner night, because they had no Number 1 Dress; they were allowed to watch. He asked to go to Germany, as he was a fluent German speaker, and thought this might be useful. Also, he was recently married. Although he got his MP, Mr Boyd Carpenter, to lobby for him, he was sent to Malaya.

He returned to England as his wife became ill, and found himself in Tidworth Military Hospital, on the surgical division.

'Tidworth is on Salisbury Plain and its sole reason for existence is that there were barracks. Each barrack "unit" consisted of an officers' mess facing the main road; behind this there were two-storied barracks for the men. The two blocks enclosed space which formed the parade ground, and in the middle there was a cookhouse and stores; behind the second block of barracks there was a service road and families' accommodation. The military hospital occupied one of these barrack blocks; the hospital served the numerous army and RAF units in the area.'

He was impressed by the Commanding Officer, Colonel Denning, and by the medical side of the hospital. 'The major in charge of the medical division was very good but could not get his membership. Working with him were Mike Gaze, who later became Professor of Physiology and Neurophysiology in Edinburgh, and Victor Rozenoer, who became Professor of Gastroenterology in either San Francisco or Los Angeles. On the surgical side there was no obvious leader – a local NHS surgeon was replaced by Mr J.G. Reid, after which things improved, and they improved farther in 1956 when Captain J.G. Williams, who later became a surgeon in Birmingham, and Captain Geoffrey Burwell, who became Professor in Nottingham, joined the staff. These two were called up with the Territorials before the Suez crisis.'

He remembered vividly accidents during the summer major training exercises on the Salisbury Plain area. 'The Army's programme was split into three terms: in the Autumn it consisted of training in small units such as platoons. After New Year training was in larger units such as companies. This culminated in the Army exercises in Summer, when Regulars and National Service were joined by Territorials. The last I remembered was in 1955 or 1956.

'I particularly remember the now forgotten Tillshead tank disaster. On a Summer day a yeomanry regiment parked some tanks on a ridge. The brakes were applied. The soldiers camped under canvas some distance below the ridge. As the night cooled, the brakes lost their grip (the tanks had not been left in gear) and the armoured vehicles rolled over the tents and twelve soldiers were killed. I was sent out to help the injured and identify the dead.

'During the same exercise some TA parachutists were instructed to jump out of a Beverley transport aircraft. The exits for the parachutists were on each side of the aircraft and the parachutists were meant to jump alternately from each side – unfortunately they jumped simultaneously and their parachutes entangled and there were further casualties. By the end of the exercise there was no space in the Tidworth mortuary.'

Laboratory posts in Service hospitals were also regularly held by conscripts. Dr R.D. Eastham, after his house job at University College Hospital in London in 1947, heard the officer in charge of his RAF intake ask for volunteers to be trained in Clinical Pathology. The other who put his hand up to volunteer was Hugh MacIntyre. Sure enough, they went to RAF Halton for the course in their new specialty. 'This was a very comfortable posting, and we were billeted in one of the Rothchilds' country houses (the Officers' Mess and residence), and the catering was excellent, RAF Halton being a training centre for catering (a dramatic improvement on the hospital food we had been used to).'

After their course, they applied to go overseas, but inevitably, were given a UK posting instead. Flying Officer Eastham was sent to RAF Padgate. The surgical specialist, Squadron-Leader Hugh Pentney, later to become his best man, told him on his arrival that, although he could not see it, there was an invisible sign over the main gate of the camp, which read: 'Abandon hope all ye who enter here.'

The station hospital had 100 beds; there was a small laboratory. Here he soon busied himself in research into the erythrocyte sedimentation rate of blood in rheumatic disorders, as an index of activity of the disease. He also was put in charge of the Continuation Treatment Clinic, (for venereal disease) which was run once a week. 'I watched the medical orderly injecting bismuth into a row of bare buttocks, and then sat down to inject neoarsphenamine intravenously into these unfortunates. They would watch anxiously how I performed, as missing the vein was very painful for them and also thrombosed that particular vein. Talking to them, I found that many of them had picked up their 'dose' during a heavy drinking party in Germany. I saw my first venereal warts. The regulars very rarely appeared on these parades – they knew how to avoid the risks.'

Next he went to bigger laboratories, at St Athan, where he studied histology, RAF Locking in Gloucestershire, and finally to RAF Kirkham in Lancashire. Here he did general duties; his stay was extended to a little more than two years on account of the Berlin airlift. But this provided another bonus. His additional time enabled him to add to his final NHS pension, and this, plus the buying of 'added years', allowed him to retire early aged 62.

Matthew Robertson qualified in 1951, but was fortunate to gain extra deferment in order to do basic training in pathology. 'I was called up in mid 1954 just after my honeymoon and left my bride at Preston station on my way to Lytham St Anne's to be introduced to Service life and do my square bashing. I joined what I believe was the second last intake of NS medical officers for the RAF and certainly one of the largest. I think there were 20 to 30 of us as opposed to the usual 6 or 7 and the drill flight sergeant had quite a time of it . . .'

The RAF officer in charge of Matthew's intake must have had something in common with Colonel Officer. 'The introductory talk when we were informed that we were to regard ourselves as officers first, gentlemen second and doctors third did not go down well with a collection of newly qualified medics and most of us quietly decided that we would carry on regarding ourselves as doctors first whatever the Service thought of it.'

He was disappointed to be sent first to RAF Bicester as station assistant MO, but after transferring to the Institute of Pathology and Tropical Medicine at RAF Halton, things looked up. 'I joined a fellow pathologist, now Professor Goudie. The time spent at RAF Halton was interesting. The pathologists declined to stay in the main officers' mess, the mansion known as "The Gilded Cage" and had managed to appropriate the smaller mess which had once been the estate manager's house and which was a very friendly place.'

Soon he found himself in charge of the laboratory at RAF Ely – a responsible post. It took work from the local civilians too. There he had to ring Buckingham Palace to find out the blood group of a member of the Royal family who would be learning to fly. His next appointment was to RAF Nocton Hall – not a purpose built building as at Ely, but wooden huts of wartime style. Again, however, the lab was a good one, with first-class support from highly trained Warrant Officers.

'Nocton Hall seemed to be the last refuge of the National Service medical officer. We were nearly all NS on the staff except for the seniors in each speciality, except me. The first CO I encountered was a veritable martinet who eventually became Director General and worked very much by Queen's Regulations, but when he left on promotion we were sent a veritable RAF character. This was a flying doctor who had been grounded for crashing one plane too many and was a mass of flying injuries but had a welcome outlook on bending rules. This was very fortunate . . . I had by now risen to the dizzy height of Squadron Leader and during an Easter break when nearly everybody was on leave I was left as acting CO of the hospital. My wife had joined me by this time and we had a flat in the village as NS officers were not entitled to marriage accommodation. We were wakened one Sunday night by the phone ringing. A voice said "This is Squadron Leader somebody or other double barrelled, the duty staff officer at Air Ministry, and did we have such a thing as a flag pole at Nocton Hall." Knowing our ENT specialist was wont to make bogus phone calls with strange sounding names, I smelt a rat and said: "Do you mean the long thing outside the CO's office?" There was a strange sputtering noise at the other end and the voice said: "I expect that means yes." "Oh", I said "we chopped that up for firewood last weekend." More spluttering. "I will report you to your CO" then went on "Do you know the King of Nepal is dead?"

"No, are you going to the funeral?"

Splutter, splutter, "have the flag at half mast tomorrow morning." I did nothing of the kind.

'On Tuesday morning I was summoned to the CO's office who was hardly containing himself with laughter. "You had a buffoon from the Ministry on Sunday night I believe. The King of Nepal is dead but never mind I've put the flag at half mast." That was all but I hate to think what would have happened with the earlier CO who had carpeted me before because my wife had been seen talking to an "other rank" wife in the NAAFI shop. Actually she was my senior technician's wife and a trained nurse in her own right, but not appropriate for an officer's wife to talk to in public.

'I remained fully convinced that my National Service had been a useful, happy, rewarding and unforgettable experience which I am glad I had.'

As well as looking after troops, NS doctors had responsibility for Service wives and their families. Dr John Aled Williams, from Llanfairfechan in the County of Carnarvon, graduated from Liverpool in 1949. Interested in diseases of children, he had two papers to his name and was working happily towards his career. He applied for deferment because of his father's serious disability. It was refused. He became the paediatrician at the central Army families' hospital in Aldershot, the Louise Margaret. His CO was Lieutenant-Colonel Norman Talbot, only the second regular officer in the

RAMC to obtain the MRCOG, and as a result, now Adviser in Obstetrics and Gynaecology to the Army Medical Services. Max White had met Talbot as a DADMS in 1948 when RMO to a Heavy Anti-Aircraft Regiment at Gravesend. From his intake, all the unattached had got home postings, all those married had been sent overseas. That winter, there was a heavy incidence of winter illness, and local general practitioners begged for help from nearby RAMC doctors. Max was anxious he might not get permission to help with evening surgeries in Gravesend, but Major Talbot sensibly told him that so long as he did his day-time duties, there was no difficulty about his helping out and that he could do what professional work he wished in his spare time.

Aled's recollections show the weight of families work there was in NS days. With huge garrisons, there were large numbers of families to look after. 'Do you know anything about measles, Blair?' Colonel Talbot asked me when I arrived to work in his hospital in January of 1953. 'No, I'm sorry', I replied. 'You will, by the end of this week', was the reply. 'There is an epidemic raging.' Indeed there was. In Aldershot District there were one thousand cases before the epidemic passed.

Aled recalled the sadness at the King's death in 1952, and the joy at the Coronation of Queen Elizabeth the next summer. Many others said the same, in their memoirs. He and all of us watched the Guards battalions drilling on the several big squares. 'On the night of the Coronation a group of us were chatting about the event. Someone asked: 'Why not go to London?' We went by train. I still remember the cheering crowd and the arm waving as the Royal Family appeared on the balcony at Buckingham Palace.'

He looked after hundreds of families. He was also, in effect, the paediatrician to the Army – supported by visits from Great Ormond Street consultants. His was an especial responsibility and he carried it with kindness and skill. It was not always easy – his lot was to see the problem cases, often children of middle rank officers' wives who carried their husband's rank with them. At times he could be very firm, if he felt standards were bad or behaviour indifferent, and was prepared to take on authority if need be. 'Towards the end of my time I was asked by Colonel Talbot to visit the wife of the General

Officer Commanding Aldershot District. A car would collect me from the (McGrigor) mess at 3 o'clock. To my surprise the GOCs car turned up with a pennant flying. Sitting in the back was a young aide-de-camp. He looked at me in amazement. (Aled was not the smartest of officers). He said: "Good God! Are you a proper doctor or an Army doctor?"

I replied: "Neither. National Service."'

His considered remarks, fifty years later, on the families problems are quotable. 'The sudden separation of husband and wife, when a soldier was posted overseas without warning, produced symptoms of anxiety. I saw one young wife who had been found wandering in the streets. She was in a fugue (an abnormal mental confusion). Although conscious, she could not remember her name, age or where she lived. She made a good recovery.

'Many wives had fears that their husband would die or be injured. Some would become depressed.

'The children suffered deprivation as a result of their mother's mental disturbance. Bed wetting, nightmares, eating disorders and behaviour difficulties would occur. If the family was reunited within a short time these symptoms would disappear.

'Separation of husband and wife rarely resulted in marriage breakdown but would become more common if the separation was longer than two years.

'The adolescent child had particular difficulties in re-adjusting to family changes when the father returned after a long absence.

'The social status of the wife was closely tied to her husband's rank in the Army. Fears of offending and fears of harming their husband's hopes of promotion were common. Anger and frustration would also occur if a wife's request to join her husband was refused. A request for a Medical Certificate to support a second application to join her husband on compassionate grounds was made. Colonel Palmer (the ADMS of Aldershot District, whose knowledge of medicine was limited) always queried my Medical Certificates but I always stood my ground.

'For those born into the Army with a family tradition of military service, the solid framework of the Army structure seemed to act as a shield against the slings and arrows of outrageous fortune, of disappointment, anguish, pain, bereavement and death. I certainly benefited from the support of Col Talbot. Any problems I took to him.'

This was a large and important part of our work. I had personal experience of working as a general practitioner in the same area as Captain Aled. I had a practice of nearly 1000 all told. Aled was our senior by only two or three years, but was wise well beyond that short interval. Following his remarks in his memoir, I can recall clearly a sad inadequate woman whose husband had been posted to Korea and had not been returned in spite of her pleas. She put her head in a gas oven on a Friday afternoon – I can still recall the address in one of the old squares in Stanhope Lines. I fished her out, got her round, and we admitted her. Aled looked after the small children. By Monday morning the man, a Lance corporal in the Royal Engineers, was back in their quarter, totally disoriented in time and space and with some Korean snow still on his winter boots.

The sportsmen had their own world. They had the enormous advantage that the Corps wanted them and needed them. I was taken off a draft to Korea in March of 1953 because I played golf.

Norman Bradford is their spokesman. Norman was a graduate from Queen's University, Belfast. He, like Aled, had spent a little more time than most in practice before call-up. His golf handicap was 3, and he had all the wit and tenacity of the Ulsterman. Posted to the Royal Green Jackets Depot, Winchester, he managed to move into the select surroundings of their mess, and worked hard as all Training Depot MOs did. Golf was his love. He played for the RAMC team. In later life he was President of the English Golf Union, and a member of committees of the Royal and Ancient Golf Club.

Until 1951, the RAMC hierarchy had for some odd reason not allowed National Service medical officers to play in the Corps team, but the arrival of the Walker Cup player Frank Deighton changed all that.

Norman recalled: 'My best story was of the Army Golf championships at Royal St George's in 1954. We had four of us representing the RAMC, Shedden Alexander, myself, Hughie Webb, and John Blair.

'We were in the top group of the Army Golf in those days – I believe now (1998) the RAMC is in a lower league. We did well – played four rounds of the championship, that is, two rounds a day, and were then in the semi-final. Old John wired to Colonel Tommy Dunn, DSO, MC, the Golf Secretary of RAMC (he did the Permanent Medical Board in Aldershot). He said; "team in semi-final. Going well." He had to do this, d'ye see, so that we could get our leave extended.

'In the semi-final we were all square and John was our number four. The matches in the AGS were played to the bitter end – so you could finish ten holes down – till the eighteenth, not like usual golf matches where you finish when you are more holes up than there are holes left. At about the 11th, I think it was, John's opponent was in a big bunker with big stones in it – the bunker was a huge one – you could hardly see the sky from the bottom of it. Anyway, this man, from REME it was, I think, said to John: "I am not going to play from here because there is a huge stone beside my ball and I'll damage my ball and my club if I play it where it lies." So he did so, he moved the big stone away from his ball.

'They agreed that if he had broken the rules, he would concede the hole at the end. Well, he came in about four holes up on John, and this meant that our team had lost by one hole. Then, in the locker room, old John told me about it. The REME officer had forgotten about their arrangement by then. Well, after a bit, we decided to ask the committee about it. I spoke to Brigadier MDS Saunders, the secretary. By now a good hour had passed, and the committee were at the bar in the club. I remember best Brigadier "Jumbo" Aitken, a Royal Engineer, who seemed to be the man to really make the decision. Well, they had a meeting, and came back with the decision that because John's opponent had moved the stone in the bunker, he should lose the hole. This meant we would have to go out on the course again and play until there was a decision – what they call nowadays a sudden death. They had to recall all the eight players – one REME colonel had begun his meal, and old Shedden Alexander was back in Shorncliffe. Someone had to get him out of the bath, and I can hear his oaths over the phone to this day. I remember, too, Jumbo Aitken laughing and saying "A tie match, a tie match, we haven't had one of these for years."

'Because Shedden had to drive back, we went out in reverse order – John played last, but now played his same opponent first, then Hughie Webb (an Oxford blue, I think he was), then me. It was now about seven o'clock. Each match was accompanied by at least one of the committee, as umpire, and we had a big crowd, all having had several G&Ts, on the first tee. You could feel the atmosphere. The REME people weren't all that pleased, I can tell you.

'Anyway, Shedden had to hole putts on the first two greens to keep the match alive. The third was then a long short hole. It's changed now. We first three halved, but found old John had had a fine tee shot, and holed for a two. So we won by one stroke at the third hole. When we came in to the club, the senior man who had been out with John's game, called out, "that's the man who had the shot", meaning John's tee shot at the third.

'But we were beaten by the BAOR Gunners team next day, in the final. We all lost. They were worthy winners. They talked about the "tie match at Royal St George's" for a long time after.

'We all got runner-up medals. I think we all still have ours – I know John and I have, and John told me that he had heard from Hughie Webb, and he still has his. Shedden Alexander died about two years ago.'

Very many years afterwards, in 1990, Lieutenant General Sir James Baird, a former Director General of the Army Medical Services, was standing outside the clubhouse of the Royal and Ancient Golf Club. He had been invited here by his former foursomes' partner in the RAMC team, again of fifty years ago. He was excited – he had not been at an Open Championship at St Andrews as such a guest before. Norman was then President of the English Golf Union, and one of the big men around. He asked the retired General: 'Aren't you Jimmy Baird – didn't you once play for the RAMC?' 'Yes', Sir James replied. 'How have you been doing, then, Jimmy?' answered Norman. 'Did you stay in?'

CHAPTER III

Trains, Planes and Ships

AIR TRAVEL WAS NOT the usual way of getting about the world in 1950. The RAF would on occasion fetch someone from one end of the world to the UK base for medical or compassionate family reasons, and it was their pride that they could do so very quickly if essential. And of course that Service carried its own personnel as it needed. The main trooping airfield was Stanstead. Stanstead was also the airport through which all RAF pathology specimens, from all over the world, passed. Similarly, the Navy transported its officers and ratings by sea. But the bulk of Army troops went by train on land for short distances, and by troopship if going farther afield. Plenty of army medical officers did go by air; Brian Ashworth flew to Nigeria in a converted Lancaster bomber. By the end of the NS era, air travel was more available – John Spence flew to Singapore in 1960 'in a nicely appointed Hastings designed for use by the C-in-C Far East Air Force. We had stops at El Adem, Aden, and Guam. There had been several air crashes in Italy that year and in an excess of caution the Rome aircraft control ordered us to fly down the west coast of Italy at a ridiculous altitude, producing widespread cyanosis (blueness of skin due to oxygen lack) and Cheyne-Stokes breathing (another feature of impaired oxygen). I thought of that day when I read (in 1999) about the death of Payne Stewart (the US golfer) and the others on board. But we all survived.'

Everyone going to the British Army of the Rhine (BAOR) went to Harwich by train from Liverpool Street station or by lorries if a whole unit was to travel. Duncan Macphie was checked by a military policeman, as he struggled with both hands full of his kit on his way to the platform, for having the belt of his National Service medical officer's raincoat undone. The National Service variety of raincoat was a giveaway to all others. Troops then went over the North Sea to the Hook of Holland, to a large transit camp. The officers' mess had facilities like a railway station waiting room, was dark and rather grim, and you could overnight there. On the cross-channel ships, soldiers slept in hammocks – I did myself as an OTC sergeant (TA) in 1950 when 'proceeding', as the journeying on military business was always described, 'to an attachment to the 1st Gordon Highlanders at Sennelager.' At the Hook there were three trains, coloured green, red, or blue. This made it easier to know which train yours was. They went to Hamburg, Hannover, and Paderborn, and beyond. Another went to Berlin.

'This was my first visit to the continent' recalled Lieutenant Robert Christian, from the Isle of Man, 'and I was amazed at the size and comfort of the steam-hauled trains. I was on the blue train, I think it was, for Osnabruck. I can still picture the sour and elaborately uniformed Conductor and the equally decorative Customs Officers in their Gestapo-like black dress and large caps, who boarded the train at the Dutch-German Border, where the engine was also changed.'

The train compartments were full of a motley collection – in my carriage was the nearest thing to a British equivalent of a potential SS man, in the person of a sergeant in the Military Police. His ambition was to become hangman for BAOR, when he would not only get a staff sergeant's rank, but be paid for every hanging he carried out. His suitcase was full of silk stockings, cigarettes, sweets, and even some jewellery – all to be used as barter for criminal exchange. He boasted that the German family he stayed with were 'good to him.' Their daughter was all too obviously used for his sex pleasure. He told me and my fellow-student: 'They'll give me a lovely supper. In an hour I'll have had a jump, see?' He snarled at the rather frightened Dutch Custom officials at the border, refusing to let them see any of his kit. When he arrived at his destination, he distributed sweets to crowds of German children as if he was giving corn to hens. I saw his local family arrive and treat him with disgusting obeisance. Their daughter looked such a nice young girl. He was one of the most unpleasant men I have ever seen.

The journey onwards was not simple. Peter Henderson speaks for all when he wrote: 'we received our travel documents to travel on civilian trains to our postings. I had to use my own initiative. In the train I had no common language with my companions and anyway did not know how much they would resent the presence of someone in British uniform. I knew I had to get to a place called Paderborn, but had no idea how big it was. At a wayside station I heard the name called out and started to leave. It was lucky that someone in the compartment took pity on me and I managed to understand that we had not yet reached the city. On arrival there I found no sign of the promised staff car (so often an officer arrived at the unit and was calmly told that he was not expected until some date in the future) for the rest of the trip! I decided to do something and tried the telephone, even though I had no German money and did not know what number I had to call! A German voice soon asked: "would I like to speak to the English speaking operator?" "Yes please!" "Would I like to reverse the charge?" "Yes please!" At last I was through to the unit to be told that, as I had not been there at the expected time, the duty driver had not waited. When he arrived all became clear – he was a Pole in the Mixed Service Organization (MSO) transport section of displaced persons. He spoke neither English or German.'

The journey along the Ruhr was an eye-opener. The whole Ruhr valley was then still in ruins. The train seemed to go for miles and miles through desolation – every building was razed to the ground. This, with the grey dirtiness of everything, made eerie viewing. It was almost a moonscape. I believe Hamburg and Cologne were even more horrific. But we did not feel particularly sorry for the Germans – after all, we knew they had done the same to Warsaw, Rotterdam, and Coventry, and they had destroyed those cities without a qualm.

Some trains had a smooth journey. Lieutenant Pentecost had 'an easy trip to Munster.' Paul Beavon had 'a magical scenic journey right across a frozen and snowbound Europe to Klagenfurt.' Some had not. Lieutenant Wellbourne reached Austria 'after an incredible tour of sidings in Europe on Medloc, the Troop Train running through the Rhine valley into Austria via Salzburg, Badgeisten and the Mallnitz tunnel before eventually arriving at BMH Klagenfurt.'

But train travel was so much the norm for British that it was 'much like home.' Dr Beeching had not done his worst by the early 1950s.

For everyone else posted farther afield, the troopship was the mode of travel. A journey took a substantial time – six weeks to Malaya and longer to Japan. A few spent their National Service time as a troopship medical officer – Captain John Lester, who so disliked his year at Lydd, was one such. 'The possibility (of being an MO in charge on a ship) had never occurred to me. To become Senior Medical Officer was regarded as a plum job as it involved promotion to Temporary Major with the pay for the rank. This did not go down well with many regular majors for they had often served long years in the army before reaching that rank and the idea of a National Service officer being promoted to that level after one year's service was unacceptable. This situation was a good example of army double-think. The post needed somebody of experience, the sort of experience which a substantive major might have but rather than admit that not enough people of this calibre were available, the powers that be created what in these days we might call "virtual" majors to fill the gap.'

But in spite of this hard analysis, he set to and worked hard and obviously with success at this new job. His record describes the other side – the knowledge of just how much might go wrong, how necessary the routine tasks were, and how difficult his passers by might be. Dr Arnold Elliot, OBE, too, has described the trials and tribulations of the Senior Medical Officer, including the amusing tale of the medical brigadier who tried to blackmail MOs on the Bombay run, to bring back Indian carpets. 'I am pleased to report', said Arnold, 'that he was found out and punished after court martial.'

Those who were part of a regiment *en route* were sheltered by being part of an established family – David Alexander travelled with the 1st Royal Warwicks to Pusan. For him, the voyage was very pleasant with plenty of free time. Enlivening moments were provided by two appendectomy operations, for the second of which he had to give the general anaesthetic, the trained anaesthetist having left the ship in Singapore!

A very few had a wife and family with them – one was Captain Hughie Webb in 1955. He recalls: 'My wife was delightfully innocent of the effects of alcohol in those days, so it took me some time to find out why she was so jolly by the time I had come back from lectures in the mornings. It turned out that the ginger ales given her by the cavalry subalterns to quench her thirst were always laced with brandy – the proverbial "Horse's Neck" – it was all a great experience.'

But for the new RAMC officer, travel was often as not on his own. As Harry Griffiths remarked, 'a trip of 11,000 miles was fairly boring and certainly coloured my view on cruising as a recreation. The *Empire Pride* set sail from a wet, windy Liverpool docks after dark. She was manned by the Bibby Line, and of modest proportions, with no air conditioning, officers living four to a cabin and pretty squalid troop decks. Laundry facilities were rather primitive. Unknown to me, a subaltern of the Durham Light Infantry was on the ship; his name was to make headlines many years later – Sir Peter de la Billière.'

Sir David Weatherall graduated from Liverpool in 1956. He was able to obtain deferment for a year and had no difficulty in passing his MRCP in the summer of 1958. The same day he passed his final viva he was due to report to Crookham for his basic training. 'My elation at having passed the exam', he wrote in his reminiscences, 'was soon dampened when I saw the miserable faces of my future colleagues in the officers' mess.' Because of an innate fear of flying, he asked to serve in Great Britain. A few weeks later, he found he was posted to Singapore.

He told of 'my social failures' in his memoir, both at Crookham and especially *en route* to the Far East on the *Empire Fowey*. 'I fear I remember more about my gaffs in the officers' mess at Millbank than the tropical medicine course. Of my social failures, probably the most spectacular, was almost to cause the death of several of the upper ranks of the RAMC by inadvertently passing them an open snuff box (a note despatched from the top of the table telling me that it was customary to pass "the box" closed. In my defence I had opened it out of sheer curiosity; I had never seen a snuff box – they were certainly not part of the Liverpool scene of my youth).'

Of the sea journey to Singapore, 'my main memory was the constant problem of being improperly dressed. Unbriefed, I had left for Singapore with a battledress, the threadbare suit in which I had taken my MRCP final viva, and an other ranks' jungle kit. When, on the first night at sea, the regular army officers turned out to dine in their immaculate blues, I had to appear in my rather battered viva suit. The next morning there was a note on my breakfast asking me to report to the commandant regarding the state of my dress. I can't remember his name; he had a hairline moustache, and an even thinner sense of humour. We looked up Queen's Regulations and discovered that officers in this predicament could wear a battledress with collar and tie. I stuck this hyperthermic torture until the Red Sea, and then, when the regular army changed into its monkey jackets, I reverted to my viva suit. Another note, re dress, appeared on my breakfast table. The ship's commandant was even more unsympathetic and insisted that we look up Queen's Regulations again to find out what officers who were in the tropics without appropriate clothing might wear in the evening. Much to my horror it turned out that they must wear a jungle kit with a collar and tie. My "other ranks" jungle jacket and trousers, provided "for emergency use" only, were packed in a small ball at the bottom of my luggage. I asked the cabin boy to press them but he was over-generous with the starch, which precipitated into a series of large white spots which covered the entire garments from head to foot. My appearance at dinner, in the company of immaculate young Sandhurst products and their elegantly dressed wives, was a nightmare which drove me to a period of fasting and obtaining all my calories in alcohol. The only night of the whole ghastly five weeks that I appeared properly dressed was at the fancy dress ball. Ignoring helpful suggestions that I go in my jungle kit I decided to attend in my pyjamas, with a sign on my back saying "The Pyjama Game." To add a touch of realism, I drew some kisses on my pyjamas with lipstick but, unfortunately, in the heat of the evening this melted and some of the elegant dresses of the officers' wives were covered in crimson daubs . . . Had the journey to the Far East lasted much longer, I would have been boarded back to the UK on psychiatric grounds.'

The whole style of troopship life came as a surprise to the young doctors who had been brought up in the war and seen nothing like it before. Lieutenant John Donald, from a life lived almost wholly in Glasgow, has told the story as eloquently as anyone could. Posted to Korea, he, like Lieutenant David Weatherall, embarked on the *Empire Fowey*, a passenger liner converted to troop carrying which was berthed in Southampton docks. The major regiment on ship was the Royal Scots, others were the advance party of the Essex regiment and 'a wide variety of odds and sods bound for points oriental and eventually Japan. A whole new bewildering and exciting world opened up. I met the English *en masse* for the first time and found them perfectly congenial. At dinner I was sitting at one end of a table at which were seated the advance party of the Essex Regiment, and a very decent lot they turned out to be. The glittering uniforms at dinner, white jackets, dashing cummerbunds, black ties and silver rank badges and medals, particularly after leaving the Bay of Biscay, were completely beyond my experience. The relaxed good manners and polished friendliness of the Officers was in considerable contrast to the behaviour to what I had come to consider as normal in my short experience of the Medical profession.

'There was plenty of medical work to be done. A Regular Major in the Medical Corps was nominally in charge of the medical services but he was seldom seen except on every conceivable social occasion and was usually reluctant to be asked for advice as he was expending all his considerable energies entertaining several lonely and unaccompanied wives. Daily sick parades had to be held for 1500 passengers and 1000 crew, inoculation parades, Captain's Saturday inspection, all had to be attended in the absence of the Regular MO who had far more important tasks to attend. Every day was filled with activity with sick parades to lunchtime G&Ts (gin and tonics), to SMG (sub machine gun, then the Sten) practice from the deck of the ship, shooting at balloons, under command of young Royal Scots subalterns. I was cordially invited to attend these practices and soon became very good indeed with the Sten Gun and very proud of my skills too!

'As the ship turned from the cold turbulence of the Bay of Biscay into the calm warmth of the Mediterranean Sea, sailing past the

Rock of Gibraltar, I was informed that my duty, as defined in Ship's Regulations, was to give the men guidance in preparation for their run ashore at Algiers. After all, they were mostly UK town dwellers who had never been abroad before, were poorly educated in the ways of the wily Arab, and the Army took its duty of *in loco parentis* very seriously indeed. Accordingly, I drew up an instruction which was distributed to the men through their Platoon Commanders while odds and sods were delivered of a lecture from me in the main dining hall attended by as many of the ship's passengers as could be mustered. The main thrust of the lecture, which was designed to scare the living daylights out of them, was to avoid a local drink, absinthe, which would send them blind and ensure that any women available to them at least, were poxed up to the eyeballs and doing dirty things to them would cause them great anguish and their balls to drop off. I made rather a good job of that lecture considering that I had never heard of absinthe until I read it up in Ship's Regulations and that I had no real idea of VD rates ashore. I felt vaguely uneasy about these tactics because I was anxious not to arouse anti-racial feelings . . . however, scaring the men off like this seemed to be the thing to do, or so I was informed.

'I have never forgotten the following morning. As I woke I glanced out through the port-hole and was transfixed by what I saw. After days of open sea I saw a line of golden arches pass slowly by only about 100 ft away. They were beautiful, French Colonial in design I was later informed, and through the limited view I had I could see neither water nor sky, only these arches glowing golden in the first light of the rising African sun. After the grey skies and even more colourless thoughts of my contemporaries in Glasgow the sight of this vision has never left me. I dressed rapidly and ran up on deck to hang over the ship's rail. The view opened up and I could see that we were in a narrow channel approaching the dock side, now I could see the water coming up to the ship's side and a larger view of the town over white houses against a sandy background which was breathtaking although the golden colour faded rapidly as the sun rose.

'Then I became aware of another strange sensation. Although I did not know it I was smelling North Africa for the first time; an acrid, threatening and pungent sensation in the nose both intriguing and intoxicating. To have two assaults on my imagination of that magnitude in the space of an hour I still regard as astounding all these years later, or perhaps this was just another consequence of my naiveté . . . As the heat of the day began to penetrate the cool of the morning these moments receded but have never been forgotten, not even after almost 50 years.

'The ship began to come to life as all these passengers ready to go ashore gathered in anticipation and the gangways were soon run out. I was nearly ready to go when some instinct warned me to have a look at Part I Orders, a list of the daily duties among other things. As I suspected the senior MO was going ashore for the first six hours and I was Duty MO until noon, an arrangement never made known to me. I learned another lesson as I read the Orders; how not to treat those junior to you. Disdain never stimulates loyalty; there are always other ways to achieve things.

'Eventually the noon hour arrived . . . dressed in a light uniform of Olive Green I hurried alone down the gangway, excited, idealistic and completely innocent and the first person I met East of Murrayfield was standing at the bottom of the gangway. He was a fine looking young boy of about 12 years, brown skinned and with dark hair and a wide, friendly, even innocent smile on his face and as I approached he beckoned to me.

'"Hey, Johnny. You like jig a jig? Come and see my sister. She is very beautiful and her skin is brown but she is pink inside, just like Queen Victoria." I reeled back in disbelief, I could not believe what my Presbyterian ears were hearing. I had heard the phrases from some of my ex-service pals but really believed they were having me on. Without thinking I swore at him in the broad Glasgow dialect which keeps appearing in unguarded moments and comes so useful at various times. "get tae . . . ya wee black bastard . . . etc." The smile on his face did not move.

'"Okay Johnny," he grinned back as friendly as ever and drew his finger across his throat. Something happened to my notions of the Brotherhood of Man in that instant. Could it be that I had just seen the real world?

'I left the docks, picked up a taxi, and was dropped in the town centre. I found this was not a friendly place and the unrest preceding the insurrection of 1956 was evident indeed . . . I was grateful for the shade of a café . . . I wanted a drink and what did I order? Absinthe, of course. I had two of them and they were delicious – the pale blue liquid turning milky with the addition of water and the new sweet smell of aniseed made an exotic change from the bitter pint of heavy ubiquitous in Glasgow. I was learning new things all the time. This lesson was never try to scare young guys off things. They don't frighten easily and their curiosity is just aroused, their anxieties heightened, and their neuroses are primed ready to be sparked off. They will do whatever you tell them not to and then worry themselves sick afterwards.

'After the run ashore in Algiers, our next landfall came when we entered the Suez Canal and gully gully men came aboard, professional shipboard entertainers who have been making a living that way since the Canal opened. They performed for the First Class passengers with their incredible conjuring tricks while their companions looted the cabins below. Arab traders sold the trinkets of the souk from their bum boats passing them up to the buyers on board in baskets on long strings; there was a great buzz of excitement and everyone had a great time. Soon we were sailing through the Suez Canal and on either side of us stretched the Eastern and Western deserts; we seemed to be sailing through a sea of sand!

'Then we entered the Red Sea and in incredible heat we entered Aden where the Pipes and Drums of the Royal Scots played the ship into the harbour with the Barren Rocks of Aden, and my God, were those rocks barren! They seemed to rise out of the sea and straight up vertically for almost ever.'

From now Lieutenant Donald experienced the trials of treating men with heat exhaustion. 'Never have I experienced such heat or even imagined it could get so hot. There was no relief when the sun went down so enterprising passengers tried to find a spot on deck where a mattress could be laid out; then, at least, nights might be reasonably cool . . . I found a tiny area of deck just outside the sick bay for Authorized Personnel . . .

'Unfortunately none of the men had my privileges and they were confined to quarters below deck in what had been originally the holds. The atmosphere down there was awful, humidity 100%, the temperatures near to blood heat and, unbelievably, no ventilation. In these conditions sweating did not lower body temperature and the sweat just poured out of people. On entering the mens' quarters, in the course of my duties, the heat hit me like something solid, the sweat poured out of me turning my Olive Greens into something more akin to wet rags in minutes, and I found myself gasping for breath. The mens' accommodation blocks were furnished with bunk beds and hammocks and these landlubbers did not take kindly to the hammocks.

'As we approached Singapore sailing through the Straits of Malacca the dark green of the land looked curiously uninteresting as land often is when seen from the sea. Even the information passed to us by a knowledgeable veteran who had been there before that this was 'jungle' or rain forest failed to excite me although I was well aware of the nasty little uprising of a tiny proportion of the Chinese population which went under the name of "Emergency" and which had taken about 80% of the British Army to contain and eventually defeat. I was not to be posted here so I remained fairly indifferent to what seemed to me to be other peoples' problems . . .

'A large number of our people, however, were at their final destination and the ship was consumed by the last minute activities of families packing their cabin trunks, clearing their quarters, and generally getting worked up to near frenzy at the prospect of disembarking. The officers who carried the biggest burden were those with wives who were anxious about the new life they were about to face and occasionally becoming agitated to the point of screeching. The passageways were blocked by bodies and baggage in a state of near chaos. Shipboard romances were being ended, occasionally tearfully but more often fearfully, in case word reached husbands who were waiting on shore. One wife in particular, an exceptionally pretty girl and the new bride of an RAF pilot, who had had a steamy and indiscreet relationship with the ship's doctor, my so-called senior officer, and several other young men aboard, was very prominent in the approaching celebrations of reuniting with her husband. As we approached our destination he flew out in a light aircraft and buzzed the ship. She responded by standing alone at the after end of the vessel wearing a light, white frothy creation of a dress which blew provocatively in the wind and waved to him as he flew past . . .' The comments of some of the watchers were not complimentary.

Many indeed were the tales of what J.P. Williams, a naval National Service doctor, called 'Red Sea Fever' or 'desperate sexual relations.' Some married wives *en route* to the East seemed to suffer from this condition in all forms – acute and recurrent. All available sites were used – Sub-Lieutenant Williams remembered a Sergeant Major who 'took a wife into one of the ship's lifeboats, thinking it was a good place to go. A bit vigorous – the lady slipped under a bench or seat – couldn't free herself – her ankle tightly stuck. Her cries were heard by the duty watch, who gallantly stood by while they tried to release her – very difficult to release as you can't lower a lifeboat onto the deck!' And Archie Hutchison recalled a particularly pretty blonde RAF wife running down the gangway to embrace her husband fondly on arrival in Hong Kong, 'after having had a most athletic voyage en route.' Perhaps the conscripts were a little jealous!

On landing ashore, reality replaced the cheerful social freedoms of the sea voyage immediately. Recollections produced anger and not laughter.

'In Singapore I stood and watched my companions disembark and feeling a strange sense of loss that I would probably not see many of these genial companions again. Indeed, one of these young officers whom I had come to like very much was soon to be bumped off in an assassination effort by terrorists. And they were terrorists, too, not bloody freedom fighters as so many tearful handwringers would have us believe, but a tiny fraction of the Chinese population trying to impose their messianic Marxist zeal on the rest of the population, but being foiled by us . . .'

CHAPTER IV

The Western Theatre and the British Army of the Rhine (BAOR)

IF THERE WAS TO BE a third World War, this was where the land battle would be fought. 'Der Britischen Rheinarmee' was soon an Army of 55,000 men permanently stationed on the mainland of Europe. Great Britain shared with the new NATO – particularly with Holland, Belgium, and France until that country selfishly contracted out – the responsibility for a vital sector of NATO's Central Front. The British sector was in the northern plain, extending to the border with Communist-controlled East Germany. The centres of troop concentration, airfields, and training areas, were thus in this part of Germany. Some British units, Royal Marines but also other fighting arms, went to Norway to carry out winter training there, as far north as Gol and Vos. NORTHAG, the Northern Army Group, was commanded by a British general.

The fall-back in defeat was, as ever in British history, the UK base, and it would be from here also that reinforcements would flow had the Russians invaded Western Europe. From a very early period, the Territorial Army was tasked to provide the bulk of the medical manpower reserves, with field units, hospitals which carried high quality consultant staff and highly trained nurses, all from the UK base. Once National Service was over, that proportion would rise to 80% of the whole medical Order of Battle. But that is another story, which will perhaps be told another time.

The largest and by far the most powerful part of NATO was the United States Army and Army Air Force; by now the USA was the world super-power. Americans toured everywhere – looking briefly at older cultures – just as the British had done a century before. But whereas their predecessors had learned foreign languages at their schools, US children did not see the need to learn any other language than American English.

The first National Servicemen arrived to a country still broken by defeat. Lieutenant Peter Bevan, later Professor of Surgery and Postgraduate Dean in Birmingham, arrived in September of 1947. Poverty and ruin were everywhere; the post-war German miracle was some way off. 'We went by train from Bentheim to Bad Oeynhausen where we were distributed over northern Germany.' At his BMH in the Hartz Mountains, he experienced the 1947-48 winter, the most severe since records began, and they were isolated by snow for three months. The winter was enlivened by a Christmas show put on by the fifteen medical staff. It was 'an all-singing, all-dancing affair with brilliant script, produced by Mike Matthews, subsequently an eminent cardiologist in Edinburgh . . . one day we were visited by the Brigadier who was medical specialist adviser to BAOR, and came to give us a lecture on a new therapeutic advance from the UK – herapin thepary. (The senior officer meant heparin therapy). After repeating this many times throughout the lecture, most of us became helpless on the floor' . . . on the clinical side, they had to treat a severe epidemic of infective hepatitis, in which many men died.

Lieutenant Bevan's account of the state of Germany in 1947 is confirmed by a different person. Rachel Gibbs, soon after married to a NS RAF doctor, recalled being with her father who was an officer in the Control Commission. They arrived in 1946. She was at once saddened by the very smell of the populace, their lack of food, and their lack of all amenities. The Control Commission was there to set up the whole range of social requirements – agriculture, food, clothing, rebuilding, hygiene, restoration of local administration and local politics. This was offered to all European countries, not only Germany. Only the French refused all offers. One thousand calories was the target diet set for the defeated. The Commission had troubles with farmers who wanted to sell to the occupying army rather that the local civilian population, because it was more profitable.

In his second year, Peter Bevan went to Hamburg – all his friends were posted away to different places. At this date, National Service was for eighteen months only. Hamburg had already its reputation as a huge brothel – 'when I first arrived, a packet of cigarettes or coffee could buy literally anything, including a woman for the night (so I was told). Hamburg was both Sodom and Gomorrah combined, and it was dangerous for a man to walk on his own in the city at night, whether or not in uniform, because of the wandering packs of predatory women. Winkelstrasse was the red-light district with a turnstile at either end, and I was interested to join a police inspection visit one evening – purely because of professional duty, of course! I rapidly advanced my knowledge and experience of VD in Hamburg: apart from cases among Army personnel and CCG (Central Control Commission, then the only government there was), the Merchant Navy supplied many customers. Following the standard run from Buenos Aires to Hamburg, 50 seamen presented the following morning in the Central Consulting Room (a squalid building just off the Little Aster inland lake in the centre of the city) with "the clap", having collected it in Buenos Aires. I referred them to the Special Centre at the 94th (the BMH some five miles away in the suburbs), and they celebrated the same evening in Hamburg, embarking back to Buenos Aires the following day, where they all reported to the medical services there – a new version of La Ronde. The histories given by our recruits affected varied greatly – "I got it caught in my zip, doctor" (penile chancre) to "I swallowed too hot a curry, doctor" (secondary syphilis).

Charlie McEwen was in Germany seven years later, from 1954 to 1956. 'While memory for recent events is not quite so sharp, 45 years ago seems just like yesterday', he mused in 1999. 'Though we did not know it, we were half way between the British Airlift of 1948, when the Russians closed the border and failed to take over Berlin, and 1961, when the Russians built the Berlin Wall, stopping the flow of population from East to West. It was the heat of the COLD WAR and the starting point of the West German economic miracle.

'The British Army had 4 divisions in Germany in the British Zone. The Americans French and Russians also had zones and the troops were armies of occupation. We administered our own bases and printed our own currency BAFV (British Armed Forces Vouchers) for duty free etc. We licensed our own cars and the zones were subject to Military Law. The exchange rate for use locally was 12DM to £1. We had 50DM to the £1 for payment of local labour. Boilerman, gardener, and hausfrau cost about £1.50.

'All accommodation was requisitioned, and in Iserlohn where I was stationed was of very high quality. Iserlohn was a Garrison town at the east end of the Ruhr, bordering on the central German mountain ranges with the ski resorts and with ready access to the central German plain . . . the Brigade was stationed in old Panzer barracks which were of the highest quality. . . nearby was the British Military Hospital.' Although this description of the barracks and the environs was enthusiastic, British soldiers were from time to time assaulted and even killed by German youths. These murders were reported by several doctors in their memoirs.

Captain McEwen was RMO to the Lancashire Fusiliers. 'We had in other barracks The Royal Worcester regiment and also the Third King's Own Hussars. There was also extensive accommodation for married families and there were about 5,000 people in accommodation other than barracks. It was therefore an excellent situation for learning about medical practice, both in the Army and a broadbased general practice for looking after children and maternity cases.'

He enjoyed his time. The atmosphere was different from the old and often dingy UK barracks and the elderly almost slum-like married quarters in Aldershot or Tidworth. In addition, he and his fellow-RMOs had the opportunity to do overnight call at the BMH. This considerably widened his clinical interest. He was happy to diagnose the specific fevers of childhood, and the general practice side of his work he found was of permanent value to him as a consultant ophthalmologist. He diagnosed a patient with meningococcal septicaemia, who recovered with active therapy. One of his colleagues developed bronchopneumonia caused by vaccinia, acquired 'accidentally while trying to blow it onto a vaccination which was in those days routine, at annual intervals, for all forces serving in the British Army. This led to instructions that all capillary tubes had to be fitted with teats for putting the vaccine onto scarification. Thus we changed standing orders . . . fortunately the MO made a fairly good recovery. . .'

Part of the BAOR year-long training cycle involved larger and larger parts of an individual unit, then a battalion, brigade, division, till finally in the year came the major BAOR exercise. Territorial Army medical units as well as teeth arms were included for their two week annual camps. Even in the 1950s the potential shortage of medical backup necessitated a significant number of these for war; at this period, all those in RAMC (TA) units had had either war experience or been former National Servicemen. For large exercises, a big area such as near Hohne or Sennelager was essential. 'Sennelager was the Luneberg Heath Military Training Area where Hitler and Guderian trained their Panzers for the Blitzkreigs. It was also our training area for Winter exercises in the freezing cold, up to the German Border. We also had the Army Dog School in Sennelager and whenever I was up there we had some insights into standing orders which forbade the feeding of food which was still suitable for human consumption, to dogs. Therefore the food had to be obtained locally from German sources and it actually cost more than double the price of the imported meat we had from Australia and New Zealand, to feed the troops. Accordingly, the Lord Moncreiff asked: "Doctor, will you come down and condemn more beef for us. The dogs are needing more food." So the dogs were well fed and the budget was balanced better.'

Henry Sandford was different from many National Servicemen in that he came from a Regular Army background. He had been 'born in the Third Hussars, in Egypt to be precise, and had spent my earliest days in India and with the Regiment in York and Tidworth. I had been taught to ride by the Rough Riding Instructor, Sergeant Weymark, who was a great hero of mine, and occasionally assisted by Cpl Cole . . . By the time that I was to do my NS, Cpl Cole was the Quartermaster. Prewar life in a cavalry Regiment was certainly glamorous, with smart parties, pony clubs, racing and hunting (the best light cavalry training).' He recalled the high profile his elders had. So for him the Army was meaningful.

He was posted to the 10th Hussars in spite of giving his sound reasons why he specified the 3rd. But it happened that the 10th were to be replaced at Iserlohn by the 3rd, so all was well.

Like Charlie McEwen, he was impressed by the high standard of the former SS barracks. Germany, even allowing for its prewar military expansion, did not let its Army slide into mediocrity of facilities as Britain habitually does. 'I was met (at the mess) and welcomed by the Orderly Officer in Mess Kit. I was given a drink and shown to my room in a small house on the other side of the road which I shared with two other officers and introduced all round. Everyone was friendly and relaxed. I learned later that my predecessor had not been a success and that they were looking forward to see if I would be any better.' (It has to be understood that by no means all faults were on the side of the parent unit or of Regulars. Some NS officers were so bad as to be an embarrassment to everyone. Nick Howarth told of how when he arrived at one unit to take over, he found his predecessor a helpless alcoholic whom the regiment had cared for kindly and quietly. Other NS doctors just did not try to fit in.)

'Cavalry Regiments are very informal. The CO is referred to as Colonel Mike or Colonel Dick and addressed as Colonel. Officers of all ranks are on Christian name terms. None is called "Sir", not even baronets. The whole regiment behaves as a feudal family with the Colonel as the paterfamilias, the officers as close relations, and the rest as faithful retainers. High ranking guests are often surprised to be addressed as "Brigadier" and offered a drink in the mess by the most junior of subalterns. (The family blood ties make for even more solidarity – as Earle Nicoll, a splendid Black Watch officer, once said to me: "if you know it's your brother or cousin who is commanding the rifle company over there, it makes a difference.") It was not surprising that morale was high in all ranks and Sick Parades almost non-existent.'

As well as being Orderly Officer once a week at the BMH, where he noticed the total preponderance of NS doctors on the staff – 90%, he called it, Lieutenant Sandford found himself with a sick parade for the Brigade Headquarters and the Queen's Royal Regiment. 'Here the ethos was different. The Queens were proud of being the "First of the Line", having been founded for service in Tangier by the Infanta of Castille (of "Elephant and Castle" fame). All activities were performed with Prussian precision with much heel stamping and everyone was called "Sir" or "Sah!" At their big sick parades, Sergeant Watritt was unforgettable. He was an old soldier who knew all the tricks. He took me on and shepherded me as someone completely wet behind the ears. He would call me to the window. "You see that private walking across the parade ground? Sah! Notice that he is not limping. He is coming to complain about his feet, Sah!" Or, "there is a company route march today, Sah! We will have plenty of customers, Sah!" Of course he was always right.'

Captain Sandford enjoyed the major Army exercises more than most. As many others found, the warm ambulance, and good stock of goodies and extras, made the RMO's Regimental Aid Post (RAP) and his personal tent quite a centre of social activity. 'Another Annual event was the "Admin Inspection" when everything was scrutinized in glorious detail.' He recalled the 10th Hussars regarding this inspection as a 'sporting event'. 'Every trooper assured me that the 10th always came top in BAOR as he ran around painting everything that didn't move. Jack Garcia, a genius of a quartermaster, had a duplicate hidden away for every piece of equipment so as to be produced for inspection in pristine condition...' Garcia was sensitive to the feelings of those from the mere supporting Corps who carried out such things as equipment checks. 'The administrative and supply tail of an army is very important as everyone's comfort and happiness depends on it. It tends to be despised by the more glamorous fighting troops and one day Jack Garcia took me aside in the Mess and asked for my co-operation. "Look, Henry, these people are very important to us but our officers cannot be bothered with them. Could you please help me to entertain them."'

But not all were posted to a good unit. Paul Beavon went initially to Klagenfurt to the BMH there, in 1954. He had qualified at Birmingham in June of 1953. His first assignment was to be MO at the Army Ski Championships at Bad Gastein. 'My instructions were to set up a Medical Room to splint any fractures and put the casualty on a train to Klagenfurt. In the event the only fractures were of family members of the competitors who refused to go to Klagenfurt (far too near the Russians for one Canadian wife) and they were treated locally at their own expense. There was a group of young women whom I can only describe as camp followers, or groupies, who moved about the Alpine ski scene living, at least partly, on the largesse of the well-off "Officer Set" in return for certain favours. They mainly had senior or retired military parents and it was not clear what my responsibilities were to them. Their problems were mainly outside my experience, such as requests for emergency contraception (the split condom or intercourse while sozzled syndrome) and the diagnosis of early pregnancy was not possible, in my book, without a supply of mature female toads (in short supply in Bad Gastein winter!).'

He had to take over as RMO to a southern English Regiment suddenly, as its own RMO became ill. He was not impressed. 'I was appalled at the class distinction as between officers and men. A Private or NCO would be put on a Charge and given fatigues for staying out one night with a girl. But a bachelor Major who went absent for ten days with a prostitute and had to be brought back by a search party, was treated with awe and respect when he recounted his sexual athletics, and frequency of same. On mess nights the young officers engaged in ridiculous and dangerous antics. One where a man was supported upside down on the ceiling in order to leave footprints across it resulted in a fractured forearm.'

He saw at once the poor level of the officers. Winter training involved trudging to no purpose in snow... there was a serious accident following total lack of care and responsibility by officers . . . he was disgusted by the plummy officer who came from the War Office to investigate, and by the determined military whitewash. This included calling 'experts' to 'prove' that no blame attached to the regimental seniors involved.

In this record, it happens time and again that the experience of National Servicemen was dependent upon the personality of those individuals and units they encountered. Those in a friendly and efficient regiment enjoyed their two years. The critical factor was where they found themselves, as will be seen now.

Peter Henderson, who had had an anxious train journey to his destination in BAOR, was in a field ambulance for his first year. The field ambulance, important as the first RAMC unit after the front-line RAP to process casualties, in this location 'occupied a former children's sanatorium at the edge of a small spa town . . . in the town centre was the brigade HQ (the field ambulance is the medical unit of a brigade and its commanding officer the brigadier's medical advisor), the NAAFI shop, the officers' club, and German shops.'

As a GDMO, his duties included medical work in nearby units – including a battalion of the King's Royal Rifle Corps, 'its soldiers were all cockneys and its officers all Old Etonians' – but his first duty lay within the RAMC field unit.

What Peter found did not impress him. 'The Regular officers were hardly inspiring. The CO was a Colonel Blimp look-alike with little obvious military or medical knowledge. The 2 I/C was a major, a charming but ineffective man who would have been liked by many patients in a General Practice, but apart from being very short of breath at rest, appeared to have neither the knowledge nor the capability to meet the needs of his army job. There was at first no Administrative Officer and the unit was carried by the non-medical Quartermaster, and the RSM. The final regular officer was an Irish RASC captain MTO (Motor Transport Officer) who did at least appear to be running his section reasonably well. Being a small unit this was not a very taxing task – apart from coping with the non-English speaking MSO drivers.'

He took part in the various field exercises. These were as important for RAMC as for all others. The unit would at once be in action should war break out. But on his first unit exercise, in a cold winter, 'I was in the main convoy and there appeared to be complete chaos when we arrived, with no one co-ordinating where each section (of the field ambulance) was to be located . . . The only apparent priority for the officers was to get the mess organized in a Gasthaus and the beds allocated before the Colonel arrived. I was sent to the village butcher to buy chops for our dinner – no compo rations for us! ('compo' was the Army field ration, in made-up meals, supposed to be eaten by all ranks while on exercise) . . . After dinner well washed down, I spent a very hot night in bed under a thick duvet in the Gasthaus. The soldiers ate in the open, had no access to the pub, and shivered in barns all night.'

His second exercise was marked by the first appearance of a new

Commanding Officer, who actually arrived just as the last main unit vehicle disappeared into its barn. '(The) Colonel was a kind gentleman and probably an excellent doctor. But he seemed sadly out of place in a Field Ambulance.'

His third exercise was during the following year. Captain Henderson had an even more unsettling experience this time. 'I have included this episode (from the following year) as it indicates that the problem of command in the Field Ambulance had still not been solved. As now one of the RMOs in a nearby unit, the 8th Royal Tank Regiment – which he loved; it was as good as the RAMC unit had been bad – I was duty medical officer for the garrison, spending the night at the MRS. A very well lubricated Lieutenant Colonel – *yet another new one* – that evening decided to move the Field Ambulance out of the barracks in its vehicles, and told me to organize it immediately. This was easier said than done, as there as no obvious call-out procedure – apart from the duty guard, all the Officers, NCOs and soldiers were relaxing throughout the camp, in the town, or in their married quarters! No officers appeared! After much swearing and shouting by the CO, somehow sufficient men and vehicles were lined up to satisfy him and he gave the order to move off, with absolutely no guidance as to the destination! The Colonel was by this time standing on the Mess balcony waving his arms and shouting – rather like Mussolini! My limited knowledge of the military told me I had to be very careful. Might I be charged with mutiny if I asked a field ambulance officer (assuming I found one) to place him under arrest and assume command? Was I entitled to do so myself, when I was not even a member of his unit? Cowardice triumphed when I thought of a third solution – I asked the colonel's permission to return to my own unit! This being granted, I actually went to my bed for the night in the MRS, hoping that I would only be called for a medical problem. Some time later I heard the vehicles return. Without my help there was soon yet another CO.'

'I did not appreciate at the time that many conscripted doctors considered National Service a complete waste of time, although some of those who joined the field ambulance after me were not very interested. I (began by) regarding it as an interesting new experience but soon realized there was no real job for me for most of the time. In retrospect the lack of direction from the CO and 2 I/C meant that only the routine tasks were being done, the Army Nursing Training for soldiers was minimal, and the largely National Service other ranks had little reason to be enthusiastic.

'A new Administrative Officer had just arrived and I decided to attach myself to him and learn what I could about running a unit. It helped me to overcome the boredom of my first year. Among the things I remember were Daily "Orders" for alleged offences, Accounts, barrack room inspections, Part II Orders, and Training Programmes . . .'

All this Peter put to good use in his long, successful and happy career in the TA. He knew what to do and what not to do, how all members of a proper unit must eat, sleep, and work together under the same conditions, if morale was to be high. He learned to take decisions quickly and sensibly, how to arrange proper training and procedures to cover all eventualities – if the Russians had invaded while he was with that Regular field ambulance, its contribution would have been a total failure. Captain Henderson's story has been told all too often – the Regular RAMC had then, as so often, those in authority who had neither the ability nor the intelligence to carry out what was so obvious. While a few intermediate ranking officers may have had a devastating time in the recent War that had left them unable to cope with their lives, or made drink their escape from the hardness of reality, this reason was noticed in our National Service doctors' account, allowance made and compassion granted.

It was not always correct to tell the truth, having regard to the Regular mind which could not tolerate any criticism, and for whom to cover up or to lie was the loyal thing to do. 'Every month a report on the unit's health had to be sent by me to the ADMS, my higher medical authority. One month I ruffled some feathers when I explained why the unit's inoculation state was not as it should be. Syringe needles had to be used many times, but the repeated boiling soon made them blunt. I threw them out when penetration of the skin got too difficult. I never received as many as I requested on the monthly indent, and the supply virtually ceased when a medical centre was opened for the new Corps Headquarters. Detailing this in my report infuriated the issuing field ambulance quartermaster, and would have hardly have furthered my career had I applied to stay on in the Army after my National Service.'

The field exercise was the mainstay of army training, and many of our contributors told of them in their memoirs. Nick Howard, RMO to the Cameronians (Scottish Rifles) and yet another who in later life had a distinguished TA career, speaks for them: 'The battalion trained in barracks in Minden during the winter, but as the days lengthened sorties would be made to the training grounds. The process led to its climax in summer when the unit would move out to the ranges at Hohne (beside Belsen) or Sennelager for six weeks under canvas on brigade or divisional exercises. I enjoyed going out into the "ulu", as it was called, but all too often I had to go back to Minden to help out. The young wives often could not cope on their own, and there would be calls for the return of their man on compassionate grounds, to the annoyance of the Jocks themselves, as well as their officers.

'An unusual exercise took place in Winter 1962. The whole unit had to bivouac out in the pine forests at Sennelager in icy cold to trial a new freeze-dried compo food which was made up for use by adding water and heating it up. It turned out that this food contained too few calories to sustain soldiers in such harsh conditions, and some Jocks developed beri-beri-like nerve pains. Half the unit including myself, luckily, were eating normal army compo, less bread, potatoes and alcohol, but we survived. The final humiliation of this RAMC-inspired study on the effects of relative starvation on fully stressed infantry was to be paraded "bollock naked" in an icy marquee to see how much weight we had lost. Never before in the field of human conflict had so many pea-sized balls been exposed to view in the British Army.

'The Cold War was serious in those days. Once after some Soviet sabre-rattling the unit was put on standby to move to Berlin. I asked the Second-in-Command whether we would be taking our war mobilization stores. "Good Lord, NO! That would be far too provocative to the Russians."

'In September 1962 the unit took part in FALLEX 62, the biggest NATO exercise ever held at that time. The scenario was that the

Warsaw Pact Forces launched a massive invasion, preceded by pre-emptive nuclear strikes in Europe and the USA. The Cameronians were part of the hostile Orange Forces of 3 Shock Army; we all had to wear steel helmets (steel topis) to distinguish ourselves from the beret-clad NATO defence troops. It was a highly mobile war, with river crossings, night attacks, and a vigorous defence by low-flying RAF strike aircraft.

'The German newspaper *Der Spiegel* leaked lengthy reports about the war, translated in the *Guardian* as "Disasters of World War III Foreshadowed." It appeared that the WP Forces had launched a three-pronged attack, with the main axis along the Helmsedt-Köln autobahn, with a northern probe into Schlesweg-Holstein and a southern attack into Bavaria: we passed quite close to home on the Grosses Moor north of Minden. This was thought to be too dangerous for armour to cross until our Orange tanks found a way through (the Ardennes, 1940 again!).

'*Der Spiegel* reported that there were 10-15 million dead in the UK and West Germany, with higher casualties in the USA, and a complete breakdown in civil defence and medical services. The upshot of this exercise was to convince the Russians that the thermonuclear scenario had to go, to be replaced by attacks with chemical and biological weapons, if ever 3 Shock Army went to war. So it was presumably a useful exercise in grim options.'

As in the UK, those in hospitals had a different life as National Servicemen from those in fighting units. Dr Graham Hunter stated it shortly: 'Because I had an interest and some experience in pathology, I was posted to the Central Pathology Laboratory for pathology in the British Military Hospital, Munster, West Germany. . . Here was provided a comprehensive pathology service for the whole of BAOR. The work was varied and interesting and I made constant forays to other hospitals in the British Sector for post-mortems and other investigations.

'There was good "in house" training and occasional promotion and re-grading all in the company of congenial colleagues. This good grounding in pathology provided an excellent foundation for my subsequent work in general practice.

'Munster was a delightful city with a cathedral and 51 churches and a memorable place in which to spend Christmas. There were interesting places around to visit and Holland was handy for week-ends.

'As a bonus I met a QARANC officer in the maternity department to whom I am happily married.'

While it was entirely acceptable for a National Service medical officer to befriend a QA officer, some who wrote their reminiscences recorded their anger at the often hypocritical antagonism of more senior Regulars when they dated an 'other rank' girl, either British or German. Some were actually threatened by a Regular officer in their hospital if they did so. 'But she's other rank status' they were told. This equates with the experience Captain Paul Beavon had.

Michael Brudenell had wanted to be a Spitfire pilot during the War. He had a haircut immediately before reporting to Crookham and was immediately told to have another one. Luckily the army hairdresser disagreed! Qualifying at King's College Hospital in 1949, he was Resident Obstetric Officer at Queen Charlotte's in 1950. A good rugby player, he downgraded his game to avoid an RAMC depot posting. After a short spell with the Rifle Brigade at Minden, and having acquired his predecessor's dog, he went through the usual course of training for newly arrived RMOs by his medical centre staff and by the battalion senior NCOs. But by virtue of being a 'GDMO with experience in Obstetrics', he was taken from them and posted to fill in for the retiring obstetric consultant in Berlin. As he observed: 'after only a year's experience!'

It was now 1951 and Berlin still showed all the signs of war. Rebuilding had just begun in the British, American and French sectors, but nothing in the Russian sector. 'Entry into the Russian sector entailed passing through Checkpoint Charley under the baleful eyes of Russian soldiers armed with sub-machine guns.' George Turner, a Leeds graduate, noticed 'how eager German girls were to marry a British soldier and thus escape from Berlin or indeed Germany.'

As far as the other Allies were concerned, 'we saw Americans of course, but the French had no dealings with us. Because of the different rates of currency, it was worth going to the Opera in what became East Berlin (remember there was no Berlin Wall until after the airlift). We saw Russian officers. They totally ignored us – there was not even eye contact. It got of course worse after the Russian blockade. The Russians had apparently been told to have nothing at all to do with Westerners.' John Bamforth had the same experience. Even as late as 1959, Gordon Macphie recalled arriving in Berlin and being told, at their introductory talk by the General Officer Commanding, 'You must remember that you are here as the victorious power.' All were impressed, in their memoirs, by the enormous number of VD cases which occurred amongst soldiers and civilians.

Michael Brudenell recalled: 'The only completely new building in the Russian zone was the very impressive War Memorial to the many Russian soldiers who had died in taking Berlin. Standing in the vast cemetery housing their dead it was a poignant reminder of the heavy price the Russians had paid – little wonder perhaps that they had no enthusiasm for helping the East Germans to rebuild.'

Next he was obstetrician in Hamburg. 'They said I would be staying in Hamburg so I knew I would soon be on the move, and so I was – to Oldenburg where we shared our deliveries with the Germans who did our emergency surgery. With only four deliveries a month I had time on my hands so often wandered into the German half of the hospital and assisted at operations.'

Next again he was 'promoted to run the obstetric and gynaecological department at BMH Hannover – a visit from the ADMS at Oldenburg led to a reappraisal of my obstetrical value and because the thirty women I delivered had done well! The unit at Hannover served a sizeable proportion of the army families in BAOR and our QA nurses included a number of qualified midwives . . . I did my first solo vaginal hysterectomy here.' Captain Brudenell was only qualified for two years and had held the equivalent of a consultant post during his National Service. He enjoyed his time, especially during his second year, when he had visits to Copenhagen with its lovely girls, Venice with its incomparable architecture, and the Austrian Alps where he and a physician colleague climbed an impressive peak.

'So why not sign on and continue the good life? Sadly the limitations of army obstetrics and gynaecology were all too apparent and the call to greater challenges in civilian life was too strong to be ignored . . . but NS gave me an insight into Army life and an appreciation of the many difficulties often imposed by politicians on a great bunch of men who sacrifice much to serve their country. Sure, there were many irritations within the organization itself and it may be that the National Servicemen did something to relieve these and bring in a breath of healthy bloody mindedness. The Army is poorer for not having such young men serving for a compulsory two years but perhaps the greater losers are the young men who these days escape that interesting experience.'

To the east was Austria, and here the atmosphere seemed different. BMH Klagenfurt at Lendorf, headquarters of the British troops in Austria and where the 8th Army had finished up after its final drive through Italy, had been yet another SS barracks. 'Arriving at Klagenfurt the full organizational efficiency of the RAMC presented itself', wrote Lindsay Symon from Aberdeen. 'When I got to the hospital I met in the office Len Rigby, Captain RAMC, (Quartermaster) Admin Officer, a very present help in time of trouble . . . "Who are you?" he said. "I'm your new surgeon", I said. "Oh my", he answered, "we didn't expect you until September" – so much for the urgency at the other end and the cancellation of half my embarkation leave.'

'The hospital was beautifully built,' he remembered, 'had spacious wards where SS men had been quartered, a reasonable operating theatre and a marvellous Officers' Mess, marble halls, elegant reception rooms, a bowling alley and a keller, in a U-shaped building surrounding a courtyard, with a little fish pond and fountain.

'We were looking after Headquarters Staff in Klagenfurt and three battalions, but the work of the Surgical Division could be regarded by no means as onerous . . . there were plenty of us to do the work . . . rockets were dished out fairly and the ship was run tight, but by 3 in the afternoon we would be sitting in Theatre House Duty Room twiddling our service caps and wondering how to spend the evening.'

He had a stroke of good fortune in getting transferred to Graz Garrison to take over the MRS. And there was further good fortune. A flat was available – a rarity for a National Service officer. Being newly married, Lindsay Symon and his wife started their married life there.

'Quickly indeed National Service passed by. Ski-ing in the mountains from Graz, Opera with Otto Wiener and Hanny Steffekin Giovanni, jolly parties and visiting the Neurosurgery Department of the University, where the neuro-radiologist, Dr Fogler, showed me the technique of percutaneous vertebral angiography – scarcely practised in the United Kingdom at all at that time. Fritz Hepner the chief of Neurosurgery, Fogler and I met many years later when, as a neurosurgeon at Queen Square and a corresponding member of the Austrian Neurosurgical Society, I used to visit them.'

Captain Arthur Wellbourne went to Vienna to look after families in 1950. 'The journey from Klagenfurt was through the Russian Zone, so travel was within a sealed train. I used to be driven all over Vienna, except for the Russian Zone, in a standard PU truck (a small type of army car) by an Albanian taxi driver who claimed to have been King Zog's hairdresser... Opera tickets at the Volksoper and the Teater an der Wien were very cheap and we used to go at least twice a week to the Opera or to concerts in the City. The State Opera House was being rebuilt at that time.'

Trieste was farther east again. Stanley Myers, a Bart's graduate of 1949, had put Trieste last on the list of choices given at the depot and found himself sent there. Alex Paton, whose father had been a professional soldier, had been posted to BETFOR (British Element Trieste Force) the year before. 'The area represented a bone between two dogs, the city being predominately Italian and the hinterland Yugoslav. Whilst open warfare was over, there were still sporadic outbreaks of violence between the two sides. A brigade of British and a brigade of American troops kept the peace.'

The work in 83 British General Hospital and in the three regiments was standard in scope and style. But here there was a romantic element not found in Germany. Lieutenant Paton wrote:

'my first sight of the city was as dramatic as I had expected. It nestled in a huge, sickle-shaped amphitheatre along the deep blue of the Adriatic . . . we passed the grim looking 15th century Duino Castle, where Dante and Rilke had written their poetry, then the striking white Miramare Castle, built in 1858 by the ill-fated Archduke Maximillian, who met an untimely death as the Emperor of Mexico, and finally the prominent lighthouse at Barcola, before entering the city itself where I was deposited at 83 BMH.' Richard Creese had a strikingly similar story, from a little earlier.

'The hospital had some 300 beds and separate villas for families and for the Sisters' Mess, the medical officers' quarters were farther down the hill.' Stanley Myers went on: 'we did a deal with our commanding officer whereby we started work at 0530 and finished at lunch, having the rest of the afternoon for siesta and beach. The city had an excellent choice of restaurants, one in particular on the escarpment above the city, with a magnificent view over the bay. The Castello san Giusto had an amphitheatre with a good opera season during the summer. Venice was less than two hours away by train, either for the day or the weekend. The Army Education Corps ran a series of courses in Vienna which were much sought after and the area around Klagenfurt also provided week-end ski-ing. It was an idyllic life, particularly when one's army pay could be supplemented by a little private practice amongst the local population.'

One National Service officer had a job in a hundred. Ian Lenox-Smith graduated from Cambridge and the London Hospital in early 1952. He began as MO to the Headquarter Mess of the Royal Artillery at Woolwich, next with the Household Brigade at Caterham – 'traditional army doctoring at its most basic'. Here he was happy but wanted an overseas posting. To his surprise, he was interviewed for a special post. 'Do you get along well with Americans?' was the first question. 'I knew only two – so I said "yes". Other factors, such as how I held my knife and fork at lunch, must have come in but this was enough to secure me the job of General Duties Medical Officer at SHAPE (Supreme Headquarters Allied Forces Europe).

Although his responsibilities 'ranged from the health of Field

Marshal Montgomery to that of A.C. Plonk's youngest child,' he found the routine straightforward with a usual sick parade starting at 0900 hrs. Individual patients varied between the daughter of the Ambassador, to a spy, to drunks in US quarters. He was asked to inspect a brothel used by serving officers and soldiers, whose efficiency and cleanliness impressed him. Because he did house calls and his US opposite number did not, he was popular in the SHAPE village nearby to Paris. Inspections of kitchen areas was charged with tension as national rivalries emerged – he had to inspect the kitchen and refuse areas of not only British, but of American and French nations as well. He had to treat with care the officer sent every so often to 'monitor the troops stationed at SHAPE' – 'we entertained him handsomely in the SHAPE Officers' restaurant and then in the British Officers' Club, and about 2 a.m. decided that he should see Paris. So we drove him into the centre of the city, visited a number of night-spots, and drove home again. We received a glowing report.' He had indeed a job in a hundred.

RAF hospitals ran along exactly the same lines as Army, but with the inevitable differences of a different Service. No reminiscences from RAF doctors who served in BAOR were received.

It has to be remembered, that the Navy had a role of great importance in the western theatre. Robin Agnew was a National Service medical officer who later extended to a short service commission, but while in the former capacity, he wrote of his experiences.

'Unlike the other Services we had two weeks at Portsmouth and then three months at RNH Haslar... then, to sea. I remember boarding HMS *Murray*, as a surgeon Lieutenant. She was my first ship. Having reported myself, I was welcomed to the wardroom and allocated a tiny cabin on the starboard side. Later, accompanied by two or three of the other officers, we had a "run ashore" in nearby Weymouth in the course of which they endeavoured, and partially succeeded, in getting "Old Doc" to imbibe too much gin. I slept very well that night!'

He described breeches buoy transfers between ships, the usual run of minor and less minor medical and surgical disease, his alarm while looking through his porthole and seeing that the ship was passing through the narrow channel between Cape Finisterre and Ushant lighthouse 'with jagged rocks clearly visible in surf at about a cable's length to starboard.' Removing crew from the stricken German merchantman IRAK, the failed rescue attempt when a seaman was washed overboard, were clear memories.

The Navy too had its training exercises. 'During a voyage through the Bay of Biscay in relatively calm sea, we had a "Mock Atomic Warfare" attack. My action station was in the ship's Sick Bay, when her decks and hull were soused in water and our 4.5 inch gun on the foc'sle fired off a few rounds to keep the gunnery officer happy. . . the noise made the Sick Bay rattle and shake and scared the life out of me! Later we entered cold and grey drizzly English Channel, which was quite a contrast to the warm sunshine of the Iberian Peninsular waters.'

He recalled the unsteadiness of his legs on return to land, and most of all, the strict orders not to speak to any press about their activities. The run ashore was looked forward to by all. Then back to sea: it was a very different National Service routine from that in Sennelegar and Hohne.

CHAPTER V

Around the Mediterranean

GIBRALTAR LIES at the western end of the Mediterranean, and Lieutenant Godfrey Burwell went there in 1955. He had done additional time in surgery, had his primary FRCS, and an MD or renal ischaemia, with distinction for his thesis, all before call-up. He later became Professor of Surgery in Nottingham. After being in the surgical division of Catterick and as acting head in Tidworth, he was interviewed, posted to Gibraltar, and given a quick course in ENT surgery.

'I flew from Blackbush on a Dakota, a civilian aircraft, as military planes were not allowed to fly over Spain. We refuelled at Biarritz At Gibraltar I was met by my predecessor, Captain Adrian Marston RAMC, also a National Service officer. The Garrison Officers' Mess was mixed in Corps and sexes. The Mess balcony had a wonderful view of the Bay of Algeciras . . . there were many cocktail parties and one notable one in the Governor's residence, but I never visited the Admiral's residence.

'At the first dinner night I attended, I put on my tropical kit with RAMC flashes but could not find my RAMC buttons, so I borrowed some from John Whitelaw, a Seaforth officer (a relative of Willie Whitelaw). I thought no one had noticed but the next day I got a dressing down by the CO for someone had told him that at the Garrison Officers' Mess dinner the previous night there was an officer wearing RAMC flashes and Seaforth Highlander buttons! I pleaded guilty and was told that this was not to be repeated!'

His surgical practice included a wide range of responsibility – outpatient clinics and operating lists twice a week. There were two other ranks wards, an officers' ward, and children's beds. At first he was the sole surgeon, with juniors, but later had an RAMC and an RN colleague. The work was full of interest and often challenge. On the other hand, being clinically senior to Short Service officers who

72

had nevertheless a much higher rate of pay than he did, he found galling.

A high point was the visit of Field Marshal Viscount Montgomery, in 1956. 'We assembled in a packed lecture hall to hear him speak. He started by saying: "I will tell you in the next hour where and when the Third World War will start" – to a hushed silence and then murmurings of excited anticipation. He continued; 'It will be in relation to China and it will be in the 1980s.' He then developed his theme and we went away mesmerized by having seen the Field Marshal, hearing and believing what he said.'

John Kirkup, who had been ordered to report to RN Barracks, Portsmouth, on 31st December, 1953, and 'told to provide myself with one Monkey Jacket (with lace stripes of rank but no indication of rank suggested!) and one pair of trousers', arrived in Malta on 2nd February 1954. 'At HMS *St Angelo* no-one had heard of Temporary Acting Surgeon Lieutenant Kirkup, RNVR.' Happily his predecessor, Lieutenant Brian Waters, RN, had been told, and smoothed his path. 'Further', John records, 'he arranged for me to take over his flat next to the Royal Naval Hospital, Bighi, and to purchase his refrigerator and hot water system, both run on paraffin. My wife arrived the next day and having a French passport, needed word from Surg Lt Waters and the Colonel of Police before entry was accepted. It must be recalled that National Servicemen's wives, even of British origin, were persons *non grata* and their husband's responsibility; thus I paid for my wife's passage and medical care including maternity surveillance and labour in King George V's Hospital for Merchant Sailors, as hospital facilities were denied her.

'Nevertheless having exchanged a bitterly cold and desolate England (–10°C) when we left for a mild and green Malta, a flat overlooking the Grand Harbour and an interesting job at twice my previous salary, we recognized our very good fortune.' Virtually the whole of his time would be spent ashore, but in his ample time off he enjoyed searching the island for its amazing range of history. In due course, he became one of the important British medical historians.

His main duty was to hold surgeries for accidents among the Maltese dockyard workers, then numbering 16,000. This took place in an underground bunker named 'B' Dressing Station where the senior attendant Joseph Caruana acted as interpreter and made most of the decisions. From time to time they were called to asphyxiated divers, although most were already dead. More major problems were referred to RNH Bigli. Many community medical problems came his way; alternate afternoons were spent screening painters for evidence of lead poisoning.

'In 1954 the Queen and Prince Philip visited on their Commonwealth Tour, and the Royal Yacht moored alongside the King George V Hospital at the time my wife Pierette gave birth to our daughter. In 1955 we were inspected outside the dockyard by Admiral Mountbatten. Noticing my wavy stripes he asked if I was to sign on permanently; my negative reply did not amuse him. There was of course a considerable shortage of permanent medical officers at this time.'

Thanks to John's wife taking French classes for Lady Grantham, wife of the C in C, and other important wives, the Kirkups received many invitations to visit French naval vessels and to receptions 'where we were by far the smallest fry. My wife told me that to visit the powder room, ladies proceeded in order reflecting their husband's rank; she was always last!' With his wife's help, John attained interpreter standard in French, then discovered that medical officers were not permitted to act as naval interpreters.

John's successor was Surg Lt Godfrey Milton-Thompson, who one day was to become a most able Surgeon General of the Defence Medical Services.

There were also RAMC in Malta. David Lloyd had hoped to go into the Navy, but found himself at Crookham instead. In July of 1958, he went to the David Bruce Military Hospital at Imtarfa in Malta. The unit was small, with seven doctors and two non-medical officers. It served not only the British troops, but also the locally enlisted Maltese Regiment. General surgical care for the Maltese was given by a visiting professor from the Maltese hospital, St Luke's, and for the British Army personnel by the RNH at Bighi. An anomaly was that the hospital and maternity departments were staffed by QARANC sisters, while the out-patient clinics were staffed by naval nursing sisters.

Cyprus was the next island eastwards. In Eric Mackay's time in 1953 and 1954 it was peaceful, and RAF officers serving in the Canal Zone rented property there where their family could live in security. Each weekend a number of flights would leave on the Friday evening from RAF Fayid to Nicosia,' he remembered, 'returning early Monday with a mixed additional cargo of food and large wicker clad bottles of Cyprus brandy. Single officers and men were free to use the facility if there was a seat and they were off duty.'

Martin Crosfill was another RAF doctor who remembered Cyprus well. He was there a year later and saw things changed. 'The headquarters of Middle East Air Force was in Cyprus . . . on the first occasion I was on leave; we travelled freely all round the island, swam from the public beaches, and walked the back streets of Nicosia without a qualm. We were shown, with some amusement, a black powder mark on a police station where somebody had planted a bomb. On the second occasion the tension was more obvious; I had been seconded to act as Station MO at Nicosia. Certain areas of the city were off limits and it was not a good idea to go wandering alone. On my final trip, the emergency was in full swing and one never travelled anywhere except with an armed escort. Medical officers changed fortnightly and the highlight of a posting was a visit (armed escort and all) to the local village, where, in a smart bungalow, one was expected to take tea with an old English lady – tea in the traditional manner, bone china and neatly decrusted triangular sandwiches. She had lived there for years, was totally unconcerned that across the valley was a monastery, possibly full of bombs and guns and things, and nothing would make her move.'

Roy Millar was RMO to the Black Watch 'when the Cyprus troubles were well on the go. We had outlying rifle companies shot at, and travel to patrol areas we knew were dangerous was difficult. We found a good way of ensuring a smooth passage for our own people was simply to tie a known Cypriot sympathizer to the front of our lead vehicle, and then drive through the townships. We never had any trouble when we did that.' Nowadays pernicious corrosion (political correctness) could well forbid such action!

Captain Paul Wellings arrived in April, 1954, as MO i/c Troops Dhekelia and families, Famagusta, from the Canal Zone. 'Cyprus was at that time an "accompanied posting" for both officers and the luckier other soldiers. The families lived at Larnaca, which at that time was a sleepy seaside village . . . entertainment centred round the "Four Lanterns", a hotel and bar restaurant, run by a vocal Anglophile Greek Cypriot; his enthusiasm for things British was later to prove his undoing. The children in the school gymnasium in Larnaca were arranged with the smallest in front and older ones at the back, behind whom youths threw stones and were shielded against any retribution by the police and later the army. . . both the church and the gymnasium flew the Greek flag . . .' He was the first incumbent of the Dhekelia MI room, 'there were two RAMC privates who ran it, or did not run it, and an RAMC corporal whose rôle was "hygiene". The former "lived in", or at least one did, Pte B . . . many years later, I came across the fictitious creation of George MacDonald Fraser, Pte McAusland, and instantly recognized Pte B as cast in the same mould. Little did we know that Cyprus was shortly to become one vast armed camp and that before the dust finally settled, 104 British servicemen were to have lost their lives.'

Sandy Cavenagh was RMO to 3 Para and took part in the anti-terrorist Operation SPARROWHAWK in 1956. He was critical of the British administrators who made no attempt to learn Greek and had a severe shortage of interpreters. 'Ignorant of what was going on under their noses, the British had not lifted a finger to correct or oppose the subversion of the children, and when we realized what was happening, it was too late.'

He described the 'domination and search' of the area allotted. After a busy and exciting first dawn and morning, there was a visit from the Governor, Field Marshal Lord Harding. 'He had won the affection and admiration of all the soldiers on the island . . . his helicopter swung low over the hills and landed in a flurry of dust on the beach . . . he shook hands with the Colonel, and all the other officers were re-introduced. He had met them all before on other operations. Then he moved to inspect Battalion Headquarters. Each department was covered carefully, a few searching questions, and he passed on. Our turn arrived. A firm handshake and penetrating glance from the kindly grey eyes. "What can you manage to cope with here?" His glance roved over our few pieces of equipment. He must have inspected thousands of Regimental Aid Posts, but gave the impression that this, to him, was a novel and interesting experience.

'"Well, Sir, we can't provide much more than glorified first aid, on our own. That and minor sick are all our equipment will cover. We hope to evacuate anything more serious to the field ambulance." "I see. What happens on an airborne operation?" "Then a section of the field ambulance and a field surgical team may come with us." So it went on. When he left, we all felt strangely heartened.'

Barry Smith came later, in September 1959. He had done extra anaesthetics, and held the DA qualification. He was unimpressed by the selection procedure. 'I requested a 3-year Short Service Commission which would have given me nearly three times the pay and entitled me to take my wife with me. In what I considered a rather crude blackmail, I was told that only 4-year commissions were available and that unless I accepted this I would be posted to Cyprus and could not be accompanied by my wife, and that there was no home leave. I was angry at this and said I would just do the 2 years.'

He worked hard in BMH Dhekalia, the fine new hospital in the sovereign base at the SE of the island which had been opened a year previously. He found it 'a contrast to BMH Nicosia, where there was little medical work, as it was closing down and was going to house the contingent of the Turkish Army as part of the independence agreement. It seemed fairly primitive, and sanitation was by latrine bucket with one flush toilet in the operating theatre.'

On arrival, he found the two Dhekalia anaesthetists had not been expecting another to arrive! Soon, however, he had his wife fly out, was given permission to live in the Turkish quarter in Larnaca, and in due course she had her baby in Dhekalia where she was given excellent care. 'The medicine was good and the atmosphere relaxed until we had an inspection from the new DDMS, Middle East Land Forces, Major-General Willie Officer, who had arrived from the Far East. A doctor of the old school, he ticked off the Red Cross receptionist for not wearing hat and gloves. We were gathered in the CO's office, where he lectured us at length that we were officers first and doctors second.'

After Cyprus, he served in Tripoli, and lastly at BMH Imtarfa in Malta, where the busy maternity unit was under command of Colonel Talbot. He shared the anaesthetic work with a distinguished Maltese, Surgeon-Major Casolani. 'I was kept to the last day of my National Service and then drove my Morris Minor back to England.'

As we all know, by no means all our contemporaries enjoyed their conscription years. Captain Smith speaks for those who did not, by his frank comments: 'Of course I hated NS, despised Short Service officers, and was a staunch supporter of the FTA club.(This club had a dark green tie with the letters FTA – fuck the army – embroidered on its bottom flap. It was worn world-wide). I had a very low opinion of the clinical competence of many RAMC specialists except for one or two time-expired senior registrars who hadn't succeeded in the NHS. The administration seemed appalling, and promises were made only to be broken. We had an aphorism that you "could only believe that something was going to happen after it had happened." I disliked the barriers between NS, SS, and Regular officers, just as I disliked those between Regular and TA.'

This same critic, who had the courage to write what we all knew, became a dedicated TA officer, commanded 217 (London) General Hospital, finally being a Consultant in Anaesthesia and Resuscitation to the Army, and an instructor in Battlefield Trauma Life Support courses. Soon after these courses began, it would be the TA medicals who would be the main teachers of this skill; they had the experience and the ability which Regulars at the end of the 20th century did not. It was the Territorial Army RAMC which gave him the enthusiasm to do this, but the relationship of TA and Regulars is, again, another story.

The Canal Zone

This was the main Mediterranean Base area. Lieutenants Andy Graham, Ronald Fletcher, Charles Hunt, and Flight Lieutenant Eric Mackay, tell the story of their National Service years there for us.

Ron Fletcher went out in the summer of 1952. He was intent on a career in medicine and told his interviewers that he intended to take the MRCP. 'So I was posted to the British Military Hospital Fayid, the main hospital for the Zone.'

'We went to a staging camp near Ismailia to await transport. I was detailed to guard an officer who had been convicted by court martial and was awaiting evacuation back to UK. I spent a night in a tent with this individual. I think with an armed guard outside. I was probably there to stop him killing himself because he was a pathetic individual and seemed quite depressed. Next morning I learned he had been found guilty of buggering his batman.

'British Military Hospital (BMH) Fayid was not an attractive place. To understand why, it is necessary to know something of the geography of the Suez Canal Zone. The canal itself, which contains salt water flowing very slowly from the Mediterranean to the Gulf of Suez, was cut through waterless desert. A second canal, called the Sweet Water Canal, and much narrower, was cut parallel to the Canal proper and a mile or so to the west and slightly uphill. It is fed by a canal which brings water from the Nile near Cairo and then divides into a northern and a southern branch. This canal system provides the Canal Zone with fresh water for all purposes including irrigation. Consequently, there is a relatively fertile strip between the two canals, but uphill from the sweet water canal is barren desert. BMH Fayid was located in this area. The term 'sweet water' is laughable. By the time the water reaches the Zone it had been heavily contaminated from all the settlements along its length. It was quite useable after purification and indeed supplied the hospital, but in its natural state stank and was dangerous. Occasionally servicemen would fall in and they would be brought to the hospital for cleaning and usually admitted because they nearly always developed a fever.

'The other aspect of life in the Canal Zone in those days was determined by politics. The existence of the British Garrison was dependent on a treaty between the Egyptian and British governments, but in about 1950 the Egyptians under President Nasser abrogated this treaty. The British refused to leave, and, I assume, reinforced the garrison. There had been some riots at the time but when I was there the Zone was peaceful enough and we could move about it freely including going, discreetly, into the towns. However, we were forbidden to go into Egypt proper and consequently we could not visit Cairo nor the Nile basin. This meant that all the troops were confined to this rather unattractive strip of desert and despite being in Egypt for an extended period, I never got to see the pyramids nor the antiquities. It was said that Suez was the arsehole of the Empire and that Fayid was 30 miles up it.

'The hospital consisted of single storey huts with some tents within a perimeter fence and, according to my recollection, only one entrance. For much of the hospital, each hut was a separate ward. There was no air conditioning but some of the wards had extractor fans. Some of the fans had broken blades and so were more or less completely ineffective. The officers' mess and quarters were mostly hutted with a few tents. I had a tent at first but then had a reasonably comfortable room and a batman . . . the officers' mess had a dining room and bar with a small garden outside with wicker chairs and a few trees, supported by watering but definitely no grass . . . the mess was quite congenial and the food acceptable . . . gin was cheap, the same cost as tonic. Wine, often of good quality, was cheap as well. Cigarettes were very cheap and most of us smoked. There was a QA mess, an open air cinema, and the opportunity to sail. The Officers' Club on the shores of the Great Bitter Lake provided meals and swimming.

'The Medical Division was run by three or four National Service MO s with about eight wards. We worked Tropical Hours (i.e. with the afternoon off) and European hours in the winter. The weather was always warm to hot and sunny. I can only recall a single episode when it rained during the twelve months I was there. It was during the night and we all stood outside in our pyjamas to get the pleasure of the feel of it.'

He had ward duty, with dysentery, poliomyelitis, rabies, typhoid fever, influenza, and the inevitable VD. Once he had to demonstrate the use of an iron lung for the benefit of Major-General Alex Drummond, when that powerful figure visited.

He thought the most interesting patients were the East African patients from their Pioneer Corps currently serving in the Zone. The African orderlies were excellent and acted as interpreters. The Africans had their own cookhouse and diet laid on.

'The African ward was a single open plan ward of about 20 beds located next the main entrance of the hospital in the extreme corner of the compound. Their illnesses were various but mostly infections, particularly of the chest. Some had peptic ulcers. We diagnosed filariasis by taking small skin biopsies at night, when the parasites were in the blood, and squeezing a little tissue juice onto a slide. The men had strong views about surgery. They would have one operation but not a second. They said that they went to another part of the hospital, one of the doctors killed them and then brought them back to life again. They were impressed with this but not convinced that the doctor could pull that trick off a second time.

'The men had very poor medical exams before recruitment so it was not unusual to have men with deformities, for instance of the hand, which really precluded them from carrying out labouring tasks. Also, I had quite a few with leprosy. We had a little side room of a few beds and kept the lepers in there while they had treatment and awaited transport home. Some of the men believed that if they spent a whole day in bed that they would die, and consequently bed rest was not often complied with.

'It was difficult to get the men evacuated to East Africa and we waited a long time for a troop ship bound in that direction. When one appeared we were told that it would not take our men. However, the ship was due to stop overnight in the Great Bitter lake opposite Fayid.' Nothing daunted, Lieutenant Fletcher went out in a motor launch and put his men for evacuation into it. He went alongside, and went aboard to negotiate. To the amazement of himself and the other MO, they had been at Medical School together. 'We had a drink together and he soon agreed to take our men. I never heard what the problem had been.' Fortunately, they were both National Servicemen, and could see sense and bend the rules!

Eric Mackay's first impressions were distinctly unpromising. 'We landed at the main airfield in RAF Fayid and were taken by bus down a dusty, bumpy tarmac road. We passed Unit after Unit living under canvas. We later found they were all Army. The day was dreich with a smirr of rain. Wind and sand met us as we disembarked at the RAF Transit Unit at el Hamra where accommodation for us, was to our dismay, bell tents. There we were kitted out with khaki drill shirts, shorts, and stockings. I was informed I was being posted to El Firdan as the sole MO.

'The journey to this small station was in total contrast to the trip a few days before. The sun shone. The Canal road northwards ran parallel to the "Sweet Water Canal" which carried water from the Nile Delta across the intervening desert to support a string of villages and cultivation about five miles wide running parallel with the Great Bitter Lake and south to Suez. The "Canal" was both water supply and sewer... As we approached Fayid we passed RAF stations of Kasfareet and Abayad and realized that the RAF lived more comfortably than our Army compatriots. We passed through Fayid, an agglomeration of Army HQ with extensive Camps and Hospital and the Airfield Unit with the main RAF Hospital. We then passed RAF HQ at Abu Suer and RAF Ismailia, all permanently hutted with trees and lawns and stone-built Administration Buildings and Messes, and within easy reach of the Great Bitter Lake. The road gave a wide berth to the large out-of-bounds Egyptian town of Ismailia and then launched due north into the desert sign-posted to a further group of Army units, all tented, round Tel el Kebir (the notorious TEK, of sad memory to some) and Port Said. Two miles beyond Ismailia and we reached our destination.

'Nothing could have prepared me for the strange appearance of this Unit. No, we were not under canvas. Administration buildings, workshops, NAAFI, Officers' and Sergeants' Messes were in stone, some with shade-providing irrigated trees. The CO's house was also permanent. The airmen lived in what seemed to be Anderson air raid shelters, two to a billet. Over years of occupation these had been extensively modified. Most had been taken well underground and were sheltered from the blazing sun by an appropriate growth of shrubs or melon plants daily irrigated by the occupants. They were cool and comfortable but lacked "military precision". Officers lived, or rather slept, two to a room – in a tin box which had been once the operative rear of a signal lorry. Ventilation was limited to two sliding windows. Temperatures became pitilessly hot. Fluid consumption in the Mess was understandingly high!

'During my brief stay, the CO's wife came out. She had once been a catering officer and had little sense and no wisdom. She was the only woman in the camp. She insisted on walking around at times, displaying an ample middle-aged body in a bikini. I think she thought she was doing "the boys" a favour. She also began to interfere in the survival mechanisms of a forsaken station, propelling her husband to produce straight little rows of oven-like huts to satisfy her sense of Service propriety. She wanted to be geometric and inspectable. The adjutant had a hard job opposing her schemes. She then turned brightly to me to condemn the men's accommodation as it was "insanitary" and infested with bed-bugs . . .

'Each day a bus (a converted Bedford 3-tonner) used to run down to the Bitter Lake and return late afternoon. It gave officers and airmen the chance of swimming or sailing or just sitting by the water under the palms sipping a cool drink. I was concerned how passive so many airmen were, and hardly used the facility. The lot of the Army OR s (other ranks) at TEK were so much worse. Their officers streamed down to the lake each day, but nothing was laid on for the other ranks. A few months after I arrived there was a mutiny, with a number of KOSBs (King's Own Scottish Borderers) sent home in chains. The wrong people were punished.

'I was relieved to know that my stay in El Firdan was temporary.'

He was next at Kasfareet, a large Maintenance Unit, joining three other medics. 'We had 50 or 60 beds, an operating theatre and with WAAFs on station and families, work was a mix of service duty and general practice . . . life at Kasfareet was well organized and busy with the stimulus of interested colleagues and a wide range of pathologies . . . malarial levels began to rise and DDT and paraffin were bought to spray the necessary lying water . . . with increased political hostility to a British presence in Egypt, incidents occurred of sabotage, the occasional shooting, piano wire at head height across roads, and we were refused entry into villages. However local officials offered to continue the control programme if we supplied the materials. As malaria levels mounted, a disguised investigator followed supplies into villages and found that both sets of paraffin were immediately on sale for cooking fuel. No spraying was being carried out.'

Most of Eric's time was in another Maintenance Unit, at Abayad, a few miles north and with immediate access from Fayid Airfield. 'It had large hanger workshops and was so designed that damaged aircraft could be taxied into the station or brought in on low-loaders. The senior technical staff discussed openly the details of building the new Concorde aircraft, and also, more significantly, the new TRS2 spy plane.

'Here we had two MOs and another National Serviceman who was a 'specialist' in midwifery and gynaecology, access to the surgeon at RAF Fayid . . . later we had two Short Service officers, and we had a lady Dental Officer.

'The advantage of this Family Hospital was not only the presence of other medics but a full quota of Nursing Sisters. So at coffee each morning we had the advantage many were denied, of easy social contact with female company. In the Mess we also had a group of school teachers, all female, as well as lawyers (civilian) attached to HQ MEAF. We had a large family "patch" as well as WAAF. There was an attached Unit of African Pioneer Corps – Kikuyu from Kenya.

'Life in the Mess was less formal than at HQ . . . An Egyptian magician entertained. Dances were infrequent, but serious. Female talent was recruited from far and near. If an officer was lucky enough to bring a partner, other than a wife, she was a prize not to be allowed out of hold, far less sight, for a moment, and if possible into bed after as well. Nursing Sisters generally managed to share themselves about but needed ingenuity to avoid being torn in half at times. The teachers appeared to have a good time having the pick of a large bunch and floating from one liaison to another with almost professional aplomb. There were several serious romances between single girls and married officers with all sorts of upsets when wives eventually came out . . . there was in the winter, a Scottish Country Dancing class . . .'

'With pressure arising from resurgent nationalism in Egypt, the political decision was made to leave the Canal Zone. Not only did we suffer a run down in maintenance, but we had to bear "courtesy visits" from the Egyptian Army. A major from their Medical Corps inspected us, detailing equipment and supplies we should leave as well as buildings. Our Staff-Sergeant vowed that after that list of demands, he would personally strip out every wire and remove every light switch before departing.'

Andy Graham went to Egypt on the *Empire Ken* in early summer, 1953. 'It was at Moascar that we were to learn our ultimate destinations. This duty was performed with rare flair by Lieut-Colonel (Flash Alf) Johnston, a real gleaming moustached colonel. I was informed, with the greatest enthusiasm, that I had the greatest good fortune to be going as RMO to the 1st Battalion, the East Surrey Regiment, stationed at Tel el Kebir. According to Colonel Johnston, the Surreys were a "crackerjack unit and please give my regards to their CO, Colonel Salmond." I did think it rather odd that a Glaswegian like myself should be inflicted on the East Surreys when one of my colleagues, John Ritchie, from Surrey, was allocated to the 1st Battalion, the Highland Light Infantry, (Glasgow's Own) at the next interview. It seemed to me just the tiniest bit possible that the Army had a special talent for putting square pegs into round holes! This impression gained some support when I arrived at the Surreys' Camp in TEK, and was taken in to the Officers' Mess before dinner to be introduced to the Commanding Officer and the others. The CO, a tall, lithe man with piercing eyes, offered me a ready smile and outstretched hand, "Welcome, Doc", to which I responded indicating my pleasure at meeting him, and respectfully added: "Colonel Johnston wishes me to give you his best regards, Colonel Salmond." At this juncture the smile froze, gin and tonics hit the floor around me, as the Great Man uttered steadily: "Colonel Salmond is the Officer Commanding the HLI, my name is Armstrong MacDonnell." By the very tones of this announcement I instantly realized that the HLI were regarded as the dregs, and I had managed to lose "Flash Alf" a friend for life. It was only by ordering a few stiff ones for the entire mess that I avoided the tumbrils for myself.'

*   *   *

In late summer, 1953, Charles Hunt came to begin his two conscript years. 'I was at Ash Vale with 125 other young doctors. There was a preponderance of young Scots in the Group, and most of them were miserable and angry at the forced interruption in their medical careers. I was different, for I was ready for a change of life other than that I had lived formerly. I had spent more than twenty five years in the warmth of home life, School, University and Clinical Surgery and Medicine – all in my home town of Cardiff. My father and two older brothers had served with the RAMC . . .'

He asked for a posting to Bermuda. His request caused laughter, and he was told there were no Army doctors there. His posting was to the Canal Zone.

First, he went to Tel El Kebir. *En route*, like John Donald, he found Algiers fascinating – he had met and talked to some French Foreign Legion officers in their kepis and colourful uniforms. 'Tel El Kebir' he recollected, 'was a dusty, featureless patch of stony desert, site of a vast Stores Depot protected by two lines of barbed wire twenty feet high and twenty feet apart, with mines planted between the wires and outer barrier, and stretching in a circle thirty miles long. Inside the Depot were dozens of huge hangar-like storage buildings in which every item required by an Army in the field was stored. In addition there were living quarters for troops sent there for security and training. Every Corps in the Army was represented, including the RAMC, which was 6 Field Ambulance RAMC.

He worked hard, set up a demonstration of casualty transport across a water obstacle, for visiting officers, and was then summoned by the fearful General Drummond. Fearing the worst, he was relieved to find that the general had heard good reports of him, and probably more important, remembered his father and brothers as a respected RAMC family. He was given the important job of taking over the Convalescent Training Depot Division. This was 'a dusty ten acres of stone strewn semi-desert on the west bank of the Suez Canal at the point where the canal joined the Northern tip of the Bitter Lakes. It too was protected by barbed wire. The Officers' Mess was enormous – capable of housing sixty officers, while the sergeants' and corporals' messes were also very big. I was joined by two officers in their thirties who would act, one as Administration Officer and one as Quartermaster RAMC. Both of them had risen from the ranks by their own talents, intelligence, and energy.

'The military duties of all staff were to receive convalescents from BMH Fayid, settle them in, make them comfortable and welcome, give them appropriate courses to encourage their early return to full fitness, and despatch them to their units when I thought they could cope with the rigour of military life once more, while catering for their spare time with entertainment and pastimes to cope with any depression . . . Food was a primary consideration, and before long we had restaurant style menus for everyone.'

His enterprise prospered, and soon had such a good name that personnel on leave were asking if they could come along to share the facilities. Their payments increased his unit's income admirably. His wife came out to join him, and loved the life.

'Lady Mountbatten arrived one afternoon, accompanied by half a dozen top brass. (I had had to stop the Sergeant Major's party of miscreants painting the barbed wire around the Main Entrance with aluminium paint. It glinted in the sun like a beacon – I explained that if the *Daily Mirror* got hold of the story, that National Service soldiers had been painting barbed wire, both the Sergeant Major and I would be cashiered forthwith!) – I greeted her and after a tour around the parade during which she spoke to as many people as was possible, in English, French, and Swahili, to my amazement, she took tea in the Sergeants' Mess and praised everybody for their efforts. It changed my ideas about the merit of VIP visits.'

The Mediterranean theatre extended to Baghdad and to the Persian Gulf. Alastair Masson, in his 1948 RAF time, had visits to a range of exotic places in that section of the Middle East. He was yet another NS officer who later had a distinguished career as an anaesthetist. In the Royal College of Surgeons of Edinburgh he became the Archivist, was awarded their Gold Medal, and was in the 1990s President of the British Society for the History of Medicine.

The other section was the north African coast, to Tobruk, Benghazi, and Tripoli. Captain Fletcher went to BMH Derma, near Tobruk, after his success at the Convalescent Depot. The time had come for it to be closed, so he had to move elsewhere. He and his wife found Derma small, with fifty beds and the staff having variable attitudes to their isolation. It had a full staff of surgeon, physician, dentist, and a Matron and six QA Sisters. When he arrived he was alarmed to find he was to be the anaesthetist!

There he completed his time. He made a first-rate contribution in the dry and uninviting Canal Zone, as many others of his contemporaries did. His discovery of a million doses of morphine in sealed sweet bottles was the high point of his last posting. So much had he enjoyed his National Service that he signed on for a further three years.

George McKelvie, later a distinguished consultant and awarded the OBE for his services to surgery, went to another Canal Zone unit, 1 Div Field Ambulance 'situated downwind of Port Suez oil refinery and seemed equivalent to a posting to hell. Boredom seemed to have afflicted those who had been there for any time. On arrival I was asked by the Colonel if I played bridge, and if so might I stand in occasionally when numbers were short. I found myself commanded to play bridge every night to all hours, with the result that at my next posting when asked the same question, I denied any knowledge of the game.

'I also received my only rebuke in all my time in the RAMC at this Field Ambulance. When walking smartly to my tent one morning, I was passed by a lady on a bicycle with her skirt riding well up her thighs. She stopped suddenly, dismounted, came back and said: "Young man don't you recognize an officer of Field Rank when you see one? You must learn to salute a person of such rank." She was a Major QARANC and I must admit that my sight may have been set to give me information as to what colour of knickers she was wearing, rather than to what pip she might have on her shoulder. Duly chastized, I only replied: "Sorry, M'am," but learned a lesson on how *not* to raise morale.'

'I also had my first of a few encounters with Major General Drummond who was on a pastoral visit to the Field Ambulance, in reality trying to get me and others to accept a Short Service commission. The answer was '*no*' but he might have been more successful if the offer had been made in a place where it could not be interpreted so clearly as a bribe. He told me he would get me a good posting to Germany within two weeks if I complied with his suggestion.

George learned that the MO in post at Tobruk was being moved, as he had made it quite clear to his CO that he had communist leanings and was therefore considered unsuitable to arrange things for a visit by HM the Queen who would be paying a courtesy visit to King Idris at that time. He went to Tobruk also, he guessed, because he had stood up to the dreaded Drummond, and a posting there would get him out of the way. (Eric Mackay, a committed Christian, told of an RAF padre who had quietly rebuked their RAF CO for making the Battle of Britain memorial Sunday a military one and forgetting the need for remembrance; the padre was posted within a week).

Captain McKelvie made all the necessary arrangements, including providing baths in the male officers' mess for nursing sisters who had no baths of their own – and being told off by his CO for his thoughtfulness! – and the visit went well. 'I ragged Richard Dimbleby about an article he had published in *The Listener*, to learn that not only did he not write it, but did not read it, before signing it. I have had a cynical distrust of the Press ever since, which later experiences have done nothing to alter. He had given a totally distorted view of Tobruk doing his best to describe a beautiful Mediterranean holiday resort.'

In June 1953 Ronald Fletcher was sent to Benghazi, to the BMH there. He found things very different from the Canal Zone, in a city built by the Italians and with remnants of sunken Italian ships in the harbour. The centre of the town had some elegant buildings with an arcade, a range of shops and cafes, and a broad esplanade overlooking the harbour. There was a very large cathedral with two large domes; it was known by the troops as Mae West. The hospital had six medical officers, a surgeon – the only Short Service man on the staff. 'There was a Lieutenant Colonel who was the CO, but he seemed to play no active part in the life of the hospital at all. He turned up in the morning, read the newspaper, had coffee with the

Matron, I assume signed some papers and then went home. I never recall seeing him on the wards.'

Captain Douglas Roy, another Glasgow graduate, went to the Libyan desert in 1948. His job was RMO to the 4th/7th Dragoon Guards at Sabratha, one of the great ancient cities of Tripolitania. He had an unusual and recordable year there, before returning to become a parachute MO with 16 Brigade at home.

'My MI room was at the edge of Roman excavations. Scientific studies were being undertaken by the combined Oxford and Cambridge Archeological Societies led by Kathleen Kenyon and Ward Perkins – the first independent studies since the end of the Italian occupation. The archaeologists had no medical cover and they asked if they could share me with the Regiment. The Colonel readily agreed and, since there were few medical needs in the Regiment, I spent most of my time with the archaeologists, acting as their GP, identifying ancient skeletons and gaining an interest and insight into Archaeology as well as sharing their social activities after a day's work. Cocktail parties were always held in the theatre!'

Professor Roy (he held the chair at Queen's Belfast) wrote a summary which sums up what most felt about their time in the Middle East. 'This was a most fascinating and formative period, wonderfully expansive after the confines of Medical School and of post-war Glasgow. I had never been out of Britain before and the heady mix of exotic surroundings, warm weather, food and drink in a quality and quantity undreamed of. The company of different minds, new and exhilarating experience all contributed towards an increasing confidence and sense of well-being.'

As everywhere else, the conscripts had varying experiences. In the Middle East, they had to adapt to countries very different from those they had known before, and the unaccustomed heat and solitude were an extra factor. Middle East Command had another small country, Aden, where fighting took place, and in 1956, came the Suez crisis.

CHAPTER VI

The Suez Venture, Aden

1956 WAS A CRITICAL YEAR in British history. It was this year that marked the end of the country's ability to launch an overseas campaign on her own; it was the end of a great era, the retreat from Empire.

In July and August of 1956, President Nasser of Egypt took over and 'nationalized' the Suez Canal. It was a calculated move which restored Egyptian morale after the USA had withdrawn its offer of money to carry out her Aswan Dam project. In Egypt, after the Canal was seized, national pride and the President's popularity rose high.

The Suez campaign resulted from the Israeli attack, on 29th October, 1956, on the Egyptian army in the Sinai desert. It has been characteristic of Israel that it makes its own position clear and harsh, if it believes its own interests are at risk. Israeli behaviour to the Palestinians remains clear evidence of that. It always seemed strange that a nation that had suffered so cruelly as a minority in so many parts of the world was so totally unsympathetic towards other minorities, Christian and Muslim, within its own borders.

The French undoubtedly collaborated with the Jews in this attack. Israeli parachutists were dropped by French planes, from their French Nord Atlas air fleet. The war was over in an astonishing four days. By then, Israeli forces had reached the Suez Canal. Their victory reduced President Nasser's standing, and his position became fragile.

Great Britain and France issued an ultimatum to Israel and to Egypt: both their forces were to withdraw ten miles to both east and west of the Canal, or the British and French would take military action. The Israelis accepted. The Egyptians ignored the ultimatum. The Eden Government in London, the Prime Minister especially having memories of Czechoslovakia, considered that Nasser must be

91

removed as posing a dangerous threat. Eden held this view well before the Jews invaded Sinai, and had already been consulting with his senior military. Political talks in London, Paris, New York and also Cairo having failed to bring about what the British Government saw as a solution, preparations for a military campaign began.

Surgeon Lieutenant (temporary acting) RNVR Geoffrey Chamberlain and later PRCOG, was in Malta. He found himself a specialist obstetrician and gynaecologist, since he had the D(Obst)RCOG! 'The Navy was very short of such experts,' he recalled, 'and I think overseas jobs were unusual for the "temporary acting".' While doing his basic training in Portsmouth in October 1955, his entry group of twenty had been lectured on how to quell a mutiny. He had been in trouble when at Victoria Barracks in Portsmouth, he had given a lecture on the dangers of smoking, the Bradford Hill and Doll report having been recently published. He had afterwards been called in by his Captain, and told quietly that the lecture was not to be given again. The Captain's reason was that recruitment to the Royal Navy depended partially on free rum issued every day, and 500 free cigarettes issued every month.

'There was a long period of building up for the invasion', Geoffrey Chamberlain remembered. 'The Services brought their men and equipment to Malta, in some cases the equipment was very dated. Slowly aircraft carriers and larger ships were converted into hospital ships while the Amphibious Warfare Squadron expanded enormously with tank landing and infantry landing vessels. They all set off in high hopes in November. History has related how the lack of support (indeed, opposition) from the Americans changed the whole face of that campaign and brought to an end British Naval power in the Mediterranean.

'As a final act of defiance, the Egyptians had scuttled many ships making impassable the entrance to the Canal. After the evacuation of troops, their Lordships agreed that the clearance of the sunk ships in Port Said would be a United Nations responsibility but done by the Royal Navy. So a large tank ship, HMS *Lofoten*, (still to be found in Rosyth dockyard) was equipped as a salvage vessel. Here would be extra engineering, electrical, and medical backup for the diving and salvage teams. They also needed a medical officer. I think the Surgeon Rear Admiral in Malta was afeared for the career of a full-time Naval doctor working for this new organization, the UN, and so turned to the amateur and made him Medical Officer in Charge of the Salvage Fleet. After all, he did have a higher degree even though it might be in obstetrics and gynaecology, a skill that would be little required in a salvage fleet in hostile waters. I was given a couple of weeks' warning of this and got into training. I learned how to give open anaesthetics with a gauze and metal Schimmel-busch mask ("always keep the damp area at the apex of the dome to the size of a shilling (10p) and this will give the right amount of vapour inside"). Just before we were to set sail I realized that my dental knowledge was thin to non-existent and we would have no dentist available. In consequence, I was sent on a crash course with the Fleet Dentist one Thursday afternoon. He taught me two or three basic principles which I had not realized in my medical training ("Always press the tooth into its socket and rotate slightly before trying to extract.").

'Just after Christmas 1957 I sadly sent my wife home to Britain for we expected to be away for many months. We set off in HMS *Lofoten* in our UN blue berets as one of the first United Nations Troops ever to go to a battle area. We chugged down the Mediterranean for a few days and when we were about 100 miles off Port Said, Nasser decided we could not enter the national waters of Egypt. After much international dispute, we were diverted to Cyprus. Here the Cypriot emergency was still on and so we were not allowed ashore officially. We set off back to Malta a week later, rather disillusioned after having had our adrenaline levels raised by this mini-campaign.

'On the way back we hit one of the storms that wrecked St Paul two thousand years ago, and HMS *Lofoten* being an empty tank landing ship was battered like a biscuit tin on the water, keeling over at what seemed to me to be enormously dangerous angles. The First Lieutenant, to improve morale, decided to hold a Mess Dinner in the middle of all this and so we had to dress in full fig and parade in the Ward Room. Try tying a black tie with one hand while the other is holding firmly onto the stanchion of your bunk while you sway

30 degrees either side of the upright; it takes a lot of attempts. We sat at the Wardroom table, which was fixed to the bulkheads, using one hand to hold onto the table and the other to eat our meal which consisted of soup (powdered with steam from the boilers put through it) and corned beef sandwiches. However, the wines were good. They were served in tumblers that we kept in gimbals alongside our places and whilst a certain amount was spilt in the wrong place, it did enhance the spirit of those who were not actually being sick.

'The trip was not all storm and later the Captain decided to allocate to each officer the organization of recreation for the crew in the dog watches. We were carrying three gross (432) condoms in the sickbay in case we went ashore. My contribution to recreation was to inflate these, float them over the stern of the ship, and get the crew in turn to shoot at them with the revolvers that had been broken out ready for the Egyptian manoeuvres that never took place. We managed to dispose of two gross (288) of condoms that afternoon. On decommissioning back in Malta the Fleet Pharmacist pointed out that it was unusual to use so many condoms since we had never gone ashore at either of our landfalls. I explained the condoms had been lost overside in a gale but for years after I had left National Service I would get a letter from the Admiralty once a year asking me to account for two gross condoms from HMS *Lofoten*. One imagines the shore of Libya littered with punctured condoms.

'After our return from this abortive voyage, life went back to a shadow of its previous self in Malta. There was an air of unreality now sweeping the Navy knowing there would be cuts in both manpower and equipment. Many of the regular officers were beginning to look for posts outside the Service . . .'

Airborne to Suez is a book written by Captain Sandy Cavanagh. He has kindly given me his permission to quote from it, as it is another National Service memoir.

He expressed the doubts both he and his friend Padre Horace McClelland had, as they talked together before OPERATION MUSKETEER began. They did not of course share them with any others.

'The marked maps from which we had been briefed, the lists of Egyptian Forces, silhouettes of Russian aircraft and armour we might encounter, had been prepared by our Intelligence Section . . . we received the news that the operation had been brought forward 24 hours, to Monday, 5th November. . . 3 Para would be leading the way, which pleased everyone. We kept our security close; an injured sapper was put in a sealed ward, as he needed an anaesthetic and we feared he might reveal secrets while semi-conscious . . .

'We could have saved ourselves the trouble. We knew some of the background to the operation: that we were one of the few British armies to have taken the field in recent history in the knowledge that our country was divided behind us; that Parliament was in an uproar about the merits of the action we were about to take. We did not know that the dubious political object of conserving our enemies' lives was being achieved by imperilling our own . . .' It would be the RMO's ninth jump.

Wounded himself, he described the process of the 'way back' as the RAMC call the route the wounded take – 'A medical orderly was attached to each company. First Aid would be given initially by the man's companions, then by the company medical orderly. He would be evacuated back to the Regimental Aid Post, from where he would pass to the Surgical Team if sufficiently urgent, or be held in the Advanced Dressing Station if his wounds were not desperately serious. Then – God only knew what would happen then. Our plans could allow for a good deal of uncertainty and variation, but the whole operation being put forward a day was not among the contingencies which we, or the Medical authorities above us, had foreseen. Today was November 5th. We knew that on November 6th evacuation of casualties by helicopter was laid on. Today was November 5th. Whether our resources were able to tide us over till tomorrow depended on the number of casualties. And we did have casualties.' He had great praise for Major Norman Kirby, their surgeon . . . 'unobtrusively, as only those who really know what they are doing can, Norman took charge.'

Captain Bruce Bailey, who was to become a noted plastic surgeon, had been with the Parachute Brigade in Cyprus and later in 23 Para

Field Ambulance, under 'the eagle eye of Colonel Alastair Young.' 'My time in Nicosia', he wrote in his memoir, 'was enlivened by association with the RAF and a desperately hard rugby field.' He was recalled at the time of Suez (having been a surgical trainee in Fayid and recalled meeting Mr A.B. Wallace and Curtis Artz, who had encouraged his interest in thermal trauma), was posted to Chester to form a FST (field surgical team), but 'after the airborne attack on Suez fizzled out, he filled a little time in London before finally leaving.' His thoughts on his time with the regular RAMC are quotable since they express what most of us thought: 'It was in general a happy one, apart from separation from my family, which gave me an insight into major trauma management, mass casualty management and "man management." I met several characters, some medical and some non-medical, who were devoted to their duties and gave more than they took. There were of course many deadbeats with inflated ideas of their worth and a tendency to overuse of alcohol. I came to understand why civilian surgeons in wartime were needed to deal with casualties ... training in casualty trauma should be an obligatory part of civilian surgical training.' He recorded, too, what must be the cleverest limerick ever written.

Flying Officer Ken Mills had a large intake, 52, with him in April 1956. He had elected to join the RAF because he wished to become an orthopaedic surgeon, and had heard that that Service had the best surgeons and the best training prospects. In mid-July, he was posted to the orthopaedic unit at RAF Hospital Ely, and was delighted. He and his fiancée hoped to get married. A week later, a new posting arrived, to take a crash course in tropical medicine and then go to RAF Yatesbury to join 215 Wing CAEF (Casualty Air Evacuation Flight), which was forming there as part of the British response to Colonel Nasser's take over of the Suez Canal.

'The CAEF was created from about 130 men led by a medical squadron leader. There were three junior medical officers of which I was one. Half the other ranks were conscripts but amongst the others were some senior NCOs with wartime experience.

'A very large quantity of assorted medical equipment arrived and

ny flight worked non stop for 36 hours to catalogue, sort and pack
ll the items into four ambulances and four lorries. The vehicles left
ne night for Swansea or Cardiff and we never saw them again. I
orget if other units were doing the same thing in other parts of
atesbury. Then followed many weeks of boredom. We followed the
olitical manoeuvres of UK, France, Israel and Egypt in so far as
hey were reported in the papers.

'My unit was left with no equipment except for our firearms (and
hat a medical unit!). The officers were issued with revolvers and 6
ounds, the other ranks had rifles and sten guns also with little
mmunition. This was said to be for self-defence. We all had
attledress and raincoats but no boots. Drilling and marching were
ot performed because of wearing out of footwear or getting wet if
t rained. There were no PT or games facilities available. Instruc-
ional lectures in a wide variety of subjects soon became intensely
oring. Regular weekend passes were issued to practically all ranks,
eaving a small nucleus at Yatesbury. After four weeks some HGV
lriving training was arranged at a nearby disused airfield at
ompton Bassett. I earned an RAF licence to drive vehicles up to 10
ons. Shortly afterwards groups of men of my flight went on daily
rips to RAF Lyneham to look at a Hastings transport, but this
ircraft had not been adapted for stretcher cases, and the seats along
he sides of the fuselages seemed unsuitable for walking wounded.
n any case, the doors were too high off the ground for wounded to
limb ladders and the stationary nose up position of the aircraft
neant that stretcher cases would be likely to slide off towards the
ail. In October 1956 part of the CAEF was transposed to Lyneham
vith me in charge. I forget the reason but it was a very welcome
hange to be at a flying station in contrast to the weary boredom of
atesbury.

'In early November 1956, the CAEF was reconstituted entire at
atesbury but was suddenly warned one afternoon to move with all
ortable personal equipment to Lyneham. This was November 4th,
 think. We travelled in the back of 3 ton trucks and were marshalled
nto groups of 38 to board Shackleton aircraft. We sat on the floor
f the fuselage with one blanket each and with our knees drawn up
o give support to the back of the man in front. Wind blew through

the bomb doors below. We did not know where we were going, bu
the late take off in the darkness at about 2300 hours seemec
interminable. We flew through the night becoming more and more
cold – my limbs were numb beyond the elbows and knees, and we
were all shivering vigorously.

'Next morning we landed at Malta and were taken in warm
sunshine down to Grand Harbour Valetta to board HMS *Ocean*, a
well known aircraft carrier. This was to be our transport. The newly
joined officer passengers (mostly RAF) were allocated camp beds in
a compartment in the stern well below the water line, accessible
through hatches and ladders from the decks above. There was light
but no ventilation or bed covers. We sailed after 36 hours – at night
– completely blacked out. The next day we could see other ships
nearby but we did not know where we were going or what course
was steered. My CO shared a cabin and here my two young
colleagues and I met to discuss plans for the resuscitation of the
wounded. The only experience available was that of the CO in
Germany two years previously where he had been on an exercise
evacuating dummy casualties to UK (in Dakotas, I believe). As we
had no equipment whatsoever apart from small suitcases in which
we carried a spare shirt and toiletries and did not know where we
were going or what sort of operation was planned, we realized we
were floundering in the dark. HMS *Ocean* seemed severely
overcrowded with the hanger deck full of helicopters and Royal
Marines with all their battle gear. There seemed to be no fixed wing
aircraft on board. All exits and portholes were screened for the
blackout so there was very little ventilation despite the ship moving
briskly. We were ordered to keep below and behind the blackout
screens both in daylight and night time.

'I think we were two days at sea when we were told action was
imminent early next morning. What action, we wondered? In
darkness the *Ocean* anchored, we knew not where. All my fellow
officers abandoned our camp beds below the waterline and lay down
to sleep anywhere there was space on higher decks. My lasting
impression of this whole week was lack of sleep and water. The ship
became very hot and we all sweated heavily, especially as we had
only thick tunics and trousers, more suitable for winter in Europe.

'Soon after midnight the ship became very noisy as the helicopters evved up on the flight deck and seemingly hundreds of soldiers in ull gear and boots were doubling about. Irregular explosions every ew minutes were said to be explosives to discourage underwater abotage divers. We were at anchor a few miles off Port Said along vith very many other ships. The horizon was virtually obscured by hipping. To the east we could see the low lying shore and huge louds of black smoke rising from the town. We could see circuits of ircraft on bombing runs. We watched destroyers firing broadsides. Chis seemed impressive to novices in naval warfare.

'Our own helicopters were running a ferry service of marines and others to land – only four or five men each. Initially they returned empty after a trip of 15 minutes or so. Quite close to HMS *Ocean* wo other aircraft carriers were anchored: the nearer was French vith many mosquito-like helicopters.

'By the afternoon our helicopters began to return to the ship with he wounded, both British and Egyptian. We were told that each arrier was expected to take 80 casualties but *Ocean* received more han 120 in two hours. During this time, we watched French helicopters returning also with casualties. One crash landed in the ea midway between the carriers.

'Since the four of us RAF medical officers had nothing to do, we offered our help to the senior naval medical officer, a surgeon aptain. He seemed overwhelmed and remained at his desk. I saw him with his head in his hands looking down on his blotting pad aying nothing. I did not see or hear of him again. Meantime a urgeon lieutenant commander (graduated only three years) and hree younger naval surgeon lieutenants were busy amongst the vounded. The sick bay accommodated only 20, the others were aid out on the hanger deck about two levels above. We mmediately found that the *Ocean* was not equipped for casualties is we were told there was no blood available for transfusion and only 24 units of other fluids. I do not know the exact truth of this, out certainly there were no fluids for resuscitation and the dental officer began to take blood from volunteers on the hangar deck, und to do the crude cross-matching himself. He had never done this before. Wounded prisoners were soon separated from our men as some prisoners carried hidden knives which they seemed prepared to use.

'I was asked to assist with the surgery. The idea of triage was unknown to all of us, so we began with amputations. The surgeon said he'd never done any before – at least I had seen a few and was able to tell him the necessary steps. The ship's operating theatre was very cramped and overwhelmingly hot both from lack of ventilation in the blacked out stationary ship and also from the autoclave which was in continuous use. We all stripped off to underpants and used cap and mask and clogs. Sometimes we wore an impervious apron or sometimes a sterile gown – these were used up within a few hours. We operated for about ten hours until 0400 and then 'slept' on the local corridors for four hours before starting again. I can recall my thirst for water. The only patient I can distinctly recall was a young marine officer with a bullet wound through his forehead. He was still partially conscious but hemiplegic. There were no x-rays, he was not bleeding and was not in pain, so I puzzled as to what to do with him: nothing, in those circumstances, apart from antibiotics.

'At the end of the next day we were all exhausted – the best seemed to be the Chief Petty Officer in charge of the operating theatre, who masterminded all equipment, sterilizing and supplies, apart from scrubbing up for all the operations.

'In retrospect, our surgery was deplorable but we knew no better. There was inadequate resuscitation, inadequate wound exposure, inadequate débridement, and over tight primary closure. Even after 24 hours, patients were declining. At this point, the CAEF was warned to leave ship at dawn so I left the operations and joined my other colleagues to enter small boats to carry us into Port Said harbour. This was a trip of perhaps half an hour, and in dim light we could see the damaged buildings, with several ships lying irregularly in the entrance to the Suez Canal. Fires were still burning in various parts but the rattle of gunfire seemed some distance away. We were discharged onto the quayside where we stood in dispersed groups holding our raincoats and suitcases. In addition our men had their rifles over their shoulders. After some time a 3 ton truck arrived to ferry us five miles to the airfield. The whole unit was moved in the course of the morning, passing through the suburbs of damaged housing and then the burnt out shanty town. The cemetery was the last structure before the salt marshes and then the airfield. We were deposited at the terminal building, all very tired. It seemed my suitcase had been left on HMS *Ocean* and I was discouraged by feeling fear at the crackle of small arms fire as we passed through the deserted town.

'Around the airfield perimeter, paratroops were dug into slit holes but the water level was only 2-3 feet below the surface. There were clouds of flies and mosquitoes. Three fresh British paratrooper graves were in a group beside the boundary. There were land mines in the sand – you could see them easily as thick black rods projecting vertically for 3-4 inches above the sand and connected in threes by trip wires. These were soon removed by controlled explosions by an Engineer officer who was killed by a mine when he had almost finished the job.

'On the afternoon of my unit's arrival, we were told that the Americans had forced ceasefire, although British Army units were 25 miles down the Canal expecting to reach the south end by nightfall. There was said to be little opposition.'

He told of being helped by the Army with tentage and food, described trying to erect tents he had not seen before, and of the next five weeks spent there, recovering swollen bodies of Egyptian dead, and feeling cut off. 'Our only news was from the BBC World Service.'

His summary, before his unit was returned to Malta, was one only a National Serviceman could write, having no fear of the Service ethos of pretending all went well: 'The unit morale, so very low at Yatesbury, shot upwards during our travels to the Middle East, but sank again in the boredom of the airfield. We were mortified by the rumours of the bad effects of our surgery on HMS *Ocean*, and rumours of very experienced but totally unemployed RAMC surgeons on neighbouring ships at anchor while we were struggling. We heard very little of the political wrangling at home or of the Hungarian uprising against the Russians. However, rumours of Russian bombers and fighters collecting on Syrian airfields also abounded ... from the standpoint of 215 Wing RAF, the whole

Suez expedition was totally haphazard, from national political policy to the smallest details of casualty reception and transport. In 1982 I was apprehensive as to what would happen in the Falklands, but most of the mistakes of 1956 were avoided, it seems.' By then, Ken Mills had become an orthopaedic surgeon of distinction in Aberdeen.

Aden

Aden lies at the southern end of the Suez Canal, and had been a British Protectorate for many years. During the century of the Raj, the Suez Canal was on the route to India. It was therefore in Great Britain's interest to guard it closely. Next above Aden was the Yemen, a small Muslim country, in British eyes full of wily dissident tribes. A treaty dating back to 1934 with the Iman of Yemen worked well, although he laid claim to the whole of the Western Protectorate. Next to the north lay Saudi Arabia, and not far off lay the independent sheikhdoms of Oman. These all had treaties with Great Britain.

In the National Service era, before the oil and gas revolution, the Trucial States consisted of seven warring sheikhdoms, with ill-defined borders.

The Aden Protectorate was exposed to tribes from Yemen, who attacked it from 1952 with increasing confidence. The Iman saw increasing prosperity next door to his sheikhdom, and this, together with the Government of Aden's proposal to federate the western Protectorate Sheikhdoms, made him fear his tribesmen would make invidious comparisons and weaken his position. They were supported by Nasser's Egypt, with gifts of rifles and money, and less openly, by Saudi Arabia.

One officer who actually had a spell within Saudi Arabia was Robert Teuten, in early 1952. He went as MO to the British Military Mission to the Royal Saudi Arabian Army. The mission was stationed in Taif, and consisted of 90 officers and men, commanded by a brigadier, whose job it was to train the Saudi Army. 'Firstly', Lieutenant Teuten recalled, 'the officers to the Mission were presented to the king, King Abdul Aziz Ibn Saud. I remember shaking hands with the old boy very well indeed. Before the resentation we had attended a feast where we all sat, legs folded, on umptuous carpets in tents and the food was laid out before us. No nplements, I think, possibly a knife . . . most of the food had to be aten using our fingers. Happily, I did not see any sheep's eyes anging around expecting to be swallowed. The presentation was robably the last or the penultimate one as within a couple of years he Americans had taken over. The closing days of Empire'.

In 1955, indeed, the Arabian American Oil Co (ARAMCO) which had the Saudi concession, sent a lavishly equipped expedition with a Saudi escort, 34 miles into our territory. It was 'politely but irmly dealt with'.

n January, 1957, the British Government protested strongly to the 'emeni Government for failing to restrain its nationals from ntering Aden territory. Attacks were in the Shaib Sheikhdom, and women and children were killed in the Qataba district. In return, the 'emenis claimed that RAF planes had bombed places within its own erritory, especially Harib. Although this was untrue, the Yemenis, with Egyptian support, made constant political allegations. The 10 rigade Group Medical Company, Aden, so enjoyed by National 'ervicemen Ivor James from Wales and Iain Stewart from Scotland, nd under the command of Lieutenant Colonel Jimmy Miller, MC, ater the first Commander Medical of United Kingdom Land Forces, nd respected and liked by all of us who knew him, was not yet in eing.

With this background, there was active warfare within the 'rotectorate. Brian O'Dowd was a Liverpool graduate of 1954 and lid his National Service from 1955 till 1957. Unlike our others, he was Irish. After being in Japan and briefly with an Australian unit in Korea, he returned as RMO to the Queen's Own Cameron Highlanders from Singapore to Aden.

'Aden was as hot as Korea was cold,' he remembered. 'At least I got diversity. Disembarked off Steamer Point, sent to Singapore ines, as it was called, on the Khormaksor (airport) Road . . . kids used to spit at us as we passed and shout: "Nasser!" I thought Nasser was a great guy and took this a bit personally. . . when the Suez invasion occurred, the mood of the Camerons was not what I'd

expected. Most officers were genuinely shocked, opposed to it all.
particularly remember one who seemed prepared to resign over the
affair.'

On 4th February, 1957, 4 platoon of 'B' Company was ambushed in
the Wadi Dhequia area of Dhala. Dhala was in the northern part of
Aden. Many years later, from a memorial service in Inverness, home
of the Camerons, their Aden RMO received a letter reminding him
of what was written in unit orders about the incident.

1st BATTALION QUEENS OWN CAMERON HIGHLANDERS
4 platoon action at Dhala 4th February 1957

No 4 platoon of B Company was ambushed in some very hilly
country South of Dhala at 1400 hrs on Tuesday 4th February. Within
thirty seconds the enemy had killed two and wounded six members
of the platoon. On our LMGs (light machine guns) getting into
action, the enemy had withdrawn. Despite the complete surprise
achieved by the enemy, the action of the platoon was exemplary. Both
section commanders were knocked out at once, Cpl Burnett being
killed outright. Private soldiers immediately assumed command of
their sections. No 23486137 Pte Mackenzie who was killed, showed
outstanding gallantry as he fell to the ground with blood pouring
from multiple wounds to his chest, firing his rifle until the magazine
was empty, collapsed and died. This young Cameron upheld our
tradition A CAMERON NEVER CAN YIELD. Due to the
difficulties of ground and failing light it was not possible to evacuate
the wounded until the following morning when they were moved by
helicopter to Dhala airstrip and then flown to Aden hospital.

THE COMMANDING OFFICER WISHES TO CON-
GRATULATE ALL RANKS FOR THEIR RESOLUTE
CONDUCT IN THIS VERY ARDUOUS ACTION AND IN
PARTICULAR CAPTAIN B.J. O'DOWD, RAMC, AND No
234711720 PTE J.A.L. DICKSON, B COMPANY MEDICAL
ORDERLY, WHOSE DEVOTION TO DUTY IN KEEPING THE
WOUNDED MEN TREATED UNDER THE MOST
DIFFICULT CIRCUMSTANCES WAS WORTHY OF THE VERY
HIGHEST PRAISE.

An account of this action would be incomplete without paying
tribute to the splendid operation of No 3 Wing ADEN

PROTECTORATE LEVIES who took an active part in the relief operations, and to the skilful flying of S/L PHILIP CLOY, ROYAL AIR FORCE IN CHARGE OF HELICOPTERS.

The commanding officer deeply regrets to announce the following casualties: KILLED 22006496 CPL W. BURNETT, 23485137 PTE H.G. MACKENZIE.

WOUNDED MAJOR CHRIS GRANT, 23134806 CPL W. SMITH, 23179544 PTE A. BLAKE, 23467337 PIPER J. McCOURT, 23479016 PTE D. SNEDDON.

DATED 6TH FEBRUARY, 1957.

CHAPTER VII

Africa

THE REMINISCENCES, records, pictures and memoirs of National Servicemen who were in Africa are complete, elegantly written in great detail, and show a different *milieu* compared with those from home, Germany, and the Canal Zone. Most had Africa as their first choice. They seemed to enjoy their conscript time very much more.

This was sometimes because there was no major enemy threat to disturb their day to day work. But this was by no means universal - the Mau Mau were active in Kenya. In general the African troops they found agreeable, and their diseases were full of newness and challenge. The senior British General staff officers seemed able, and their own RAMC commanding officers likeable and helpful. There seemed less red tape and less in-fighting. The native medical orderlies were experienced and dedicated.

Also, they had the background support and friendship of British colonial administrators and of the much more experienced medical and surgical government staff. They did not meet the too-often less-than-inspiring regular RAMC specialists. For practical purposes, all work was done by National Service, with the help of skilled surgeons and physicians, colonial service or missionary. They also had the social scene that went with the British overseas. Several were most impressed with the hard work and dedication of the British officials. The PC (Pernicious Corrupt) attacks on all 'Empire' doings by aggressive liberal denigrators in the later 20th century are false, in the estimation of these young doctors, who certainly had no axe to grind. They had the thrill of, first, the journey to get to their destination – in 1949 John Tallack wrote: 'we landed at the end of our first leg at Castel Benito, near Tripoli in North Africa, and for the first time since my posting came through my spirits lifted, for the sun shone, the air was fresh and the spring flowers were

looming . . . we spent a day there, and in the evening our Handley
age Hastings left for the second leg of our journey, over the Sahara
o Kaduna in Nigeria. The immensity of the Sahara was brought
ome to me as for hour after hour we droned through the night
ver nothingness. Little time was spent in Kaduna – just enough for
efuelling before flying on to 37 (WA) Military Hospital, Accra, our
inal destination . . . I met some delightful Army doctors, fellow
National Service.'

And in 1954, Lieutenant George Pollock from Aberdeen, after a
leak eight months in Germany, decided to ask for a posting to
Africa. 'I made the mistake of trying to get things done through
official channels and encountered total obstruction: "Not worth
moving a National Serviceman".' But by a happy and fortuitous set
f circumstances, he got the chance to go to East Africa. He went by
hip, on the *Empire Halladale*, by way of the Canal, Aden, and
Mombasa.

'As the ship lurched towards the Levant, the sky became blue, and
here was a general feeling that very foreign parts would soon be
ppearing . . . the first was the classical façade of Alexandria, then the
palm trees of Port Said . . . then to Mombasa . . . The 300-mile train
ourney from Mombasa to Nairobi was full of interest, climbing
lowly (sometimes at no more than walking pace) from sea level to
ive and a half thousand feet. The slow pace had its own mythology
– or could it be true that a lion could jump aboard, quietly lunch off
ne of the passengers, and leave the train farther up the line? People
wore there were many authenticated cases. At one point travelling
hrough *Wakamba* territory, Bill, (the regimental paymaster of the
st Battalion, King's Shropshire Light Infantry, whose RMO George
ow was) who was gazing out of the window, called out to me:
'What lovely brown eyes she's got." A beautiful young woman,
naked from the waist up, gave us an enormous smile and a wave and
alled out: "Jambo!" I had learned my first Swahili word, although I
was to become proficient in the language, initially by studying *Up-
Country Swahili*, a really useful Army Issue.'

There was, of course, military danger in Kenya at this date.
George Pollock, again, recorded in his reminiscence: 'Our camp at
Muthaiga, on the old Nairobi racecourse, reminded me of scout

camping holidays of ten years previously. Of course there wer
differences; in the Boy Scouts we didn't carry a .38 revolver wit
"one up the spout" as the saying went, and we didn't have to stan
to just before dawn in case of a murderous attack by Mau Ma
brandishing pangas. (In fact, I never saw a living Mau Mau, on
literally heaps of dead ones in the backs of trucks returning from
sorties in the Aberdare forest.)

'When we did move up country, the First Battalion, King'
Shropshire Light Infantry proved the truth of what I had alway
assumed was a stereotype myth i.e. the officers dined in, in Blues o
Dinner jacket, in the jungle, four times a week. Two of the four wer
compulsory, but I skipped the others and read by torch in my tent.'

All National Servicemen had virtually the same daily routine –
very early start to the sick parade, sometimes visits to Britis
families, the inevitable inoculations and vaccinations, examination c
blood and stool for parasites, and plenty of free time after lunch
Here the great difference to home was the warmth and the livestoc
– domestic and wild. An extra was the chance of leaving the statio
on recruiting parties, or of going to see grand and memorabl
scenery when on leave.

George Pollock had a special bonus. 'As RMO I had to get up a
0600 to take a sick parade at 06.30. The reason for this early parad
was so that those seen but returned to duty were able to procee
forthwith on platoon patrols; in other words, no one except th
genuinely sick could escape the potential horrors of the forest, wher
every creaking bamboo tree might mean imminent danger.

'Because I had to be up and about long before any of the othe
officers, I was able to negotiate a deal with the CO by which, or
certain mornings, provided I was able to arrange cover by
colleague, I was allowed to have unofficial flying lessons at the loca
RAF station. Provided I put a shilling in the Sergeants' Mess box o
each occasion, I was welcome to sit in the rear seat of a Harvard and
even, in due course, learned to handle the plane not too badly (in
the air only, never taking off or landing). My most exciting memor
of personally having control was flying low over Lake Elmenteit
and scattering the flamingos to either side, rather like the Biblica
description of the Parting of the Red Sea. The most terrifyin

moment was when the pilot dived inside the crater of the extinct
volcano Ol Longnot, and did a sort of "wall of death" circuit with
wings vertical.'

With three months to go before his demobilization, he was
offered a transfer to the BMH Nairobi by his ADMS. This sensible
idea was that the last few months of his service should be spent in a
hospital, as preparation for return to work in the NHS.

'Just as I was preparing to be transferred, something unexpected
happened. The OC Base Hospital Nakuru, about 90 miles up the
Rift Valley, went sick with severe glandular fever, and I had to go
and take over. The hospital was 50-bedded and provided both out-
patient and in-patient care for the African recruits at the Base Camp
- a sort of miniature Aldershot. To assist me I had the part-time
services of a very pleasant female civilian doctor who, as chance
would have it had graduated at the same medical school as myself.
We split the out-patient workload (by far the major part) in the
mornings and I took responsibility for the in-patients. To help with
the latter, I had the nursing support of a Wardmaster, Sergeant
Leonard Omondi, and other staff of the East African Army Nursing
Corps. Although I spent only a month there, it was an incredible
experience; Sergeant Omondi, of the *Jaluo* tribe, was a highly
intelligent and hard-working WO (Warrant Officer), with an
enormous smile and the capacity to make the hospital run like
clockwork. He taught me to take a brief history in Swahili, e.g.

"Shauiri gani?"

"Ni muda gani tangu ulipopata hii?"

"Unahara?"

"Unasikia damu kamnakajoa?"

"Nionyesha mahali unasikia uchungu."

(What's the matter with you? Are you any worse or is the pain
more widespread than your last visit? Are you passing blood in your
urine? No but I do know that I feel sore pain here in the same
place.)

Not everywhere were the British welcome. Lieutenant Peter Clarke,
not an RAMC but an RADC National Serviceman, was in Kenya in
early 1953. On his way to his posting to the Station Hospital at

Nyeri, he found the Kikuyu people friendly, but nearer Nyeri, 'I
disturbed me a little that in a few areas the natives did not smile and
give the greeting "Jambo Bwana", but would pass by sullenly, aver
their gaze, and spit on the ground as we passed, quite obviously
disapproving of our presence . . . it took, I recollect, about four
hours to reach Nyeri. The Station Hospital was on a knoll outside
the village, within a barbed wire perimeter fence. Also within the
fence was a stone built European school which had been evacuated
during the Emergency. It did have a useful anaesthetic room and
theatre.

'I noticed, carved into the wooden frame round the entrance to
the mess tent, the words FTA in prominent letters. Like all National
Service officers, and presumably the Regulars, I knew what the
letters stood for. I think all National Servicemen to a man did not
take the Army, its customs and ethos, seriously.

'I mention this lettering because the famously aggressive General
Drummond late RAMC was doing a tour of inspection of the
medical units in East Africa a few months later. On approaching the
mess tent he paused at the entrance, looking at the letters FTA.
"What does that stand for?" he asked. I am sure he was trying to
embarrass the officers, but one of them, I think it was Captain
Worsley, quick as a flash, said: "Future Territorial Army Sir." I think
the general realized he had been outsmarted and nothing further was
said!'

Ernest Walton graduated earlier, in 1949 from Durham. At the
date of his entry, in early 1950 – he did only a house surgeon's job
then decided to get his NS over – the conscription period was then
still only eighteen months. He opted for the Middle East, with the
hope of getting to Africa. He could not be sure, and was on
tenterhooks when the small group of very newly arrived National
Servicemen were awaiting their fate in Fayid. The ADMS
announced that he usually posted on an alphabetical basis. 'I
groaned inwardly', remembered Ernest Walton, 'I had set my heart
on East Africa and it looked as if I (surname Walton) was to be
condemned to suffer the Canal Zone, which at the time had a bad
reputation.' But to his astonishment, the ADMS decided to reverse
his usual routine and start at the end of the alphabet. Walton found

himself *en route* for East Africa! 'Fayid seemed a dismal place – rows and rows of dreary huts and little greenery. . .'

As there was a delay of a fortnight before the next troopship was due to leave, they asked if they could visit Cairo – and their request was granted. This leave was then cancelled, and they were ordered to fly. But they did manage fine dinners in Cairo, and plenty of time there to see around, including visits to King Farouk's Palace and Shepheards Hotel, before their plane left. They felt privileged, and compared to so many others, they were. And they flew first class to Khartoum!

'Kenya seemed very pleasant from above; we flew in a BAOC Solent "Speedbird" flying boat, and as we descended into the Rift Valley, a pink sheet detached itself from one lake – a mass of thousands of flamingos. We landed uneventfully on Lake Naivisha and were struck with the similarity to Scotland . . . the sixty miles to Nairobi was soon accomplished on a good road . . .

'On Thursday 1st June the three of us went in the hospital car to British Military Headquarters in the centre of Nairobi to see the DDMS Brigadier McNamara, a rather pleasant, if a bit crotchety, old soul. Lieut Neill we already knew was going to the Station Hospital as a junior surgeon (with all of two years' experience). We were told there were only two vacancies for general duties medical officers, one in Mauritius, the other at Nanyuki. We tossed for it and I got Nanyuki, which I was told was in a very beautiful area of the White Highlands and was one of the best stations, if not the best, in East Africa. I had visions of safaris into the Masai Mara, of climbing Mount Kenya, of leave at Mombasa on the coast! I was just about to go down to the town the next afternoon to buy a fishing rod, having scrounged a lift, when I was intercepted to take a telephone call – "this is Brigadier McNamara's office. You have been posted to British Somaliland to take up duty as RMO to the Somaliland Scouts and will fly there on Sunday. Transport will pick you up at 9 a.m." My world came crashing down! My image of Somaliland was of desert and heat and desolation, in which one could travel 200 miles without meeting a soul.'

Paul Wellings described the role of the Somaliland Scouts, for he too went there, although later than Ernest Walton. 'The Regimental

name suggested an irregular and rather glamorous Force, with
overtones of the North West Frontier in India. The regimental
badge, of an "S" surmounting crossed spears, painted on the mud
guards of the vehicles, heightened the impression, made even more
by the tall, thin askari in kullah and khaki pugri. The Scouts' role
was really that of aid to the Civil Power. In no way could the Scouts
resist, say, an invasion from Ethiopia, or a full-blooded uprising in
the country itself. In these circumstances, it was expected to do the
best it could and hang on till help came from elsewhere. In addition
to the Scouts there was a Police Force, which was armed, and the
District Commissioners also had armed Illalos under their
command.' 'The battalion,' Lieutenant John Gibson recorded, 'was
disposed widely, HQ and one rifle company in Hargeisa (4000 ft),
one company at Burao (3000 ft), two companies on outstation in
the southern boundary area, and the Depot a very pleasant hill
station at Borama (5000 ft). Normally no troops were stationed in
the hot humid coastal plain.'

Lieutenant Walton had a day to take over from his predecessor,
whom he found was Captain Bob Marley, from the year above him
at Newcastle. He met the Colonial Service doctor Dr Suarez, signed
for the usual medical stores and drugs, received the keys of the
refrigerator and the dangerous drugs safe. At once, he was off on a
recruiting drive.

The affable Commanding Officer, Lieutenant Colonel Humphrey
French, had written his orders with Captain Marley's name included,
but as Captain Marley was at the very end of his two years, and had
to return home, a replacement had to be found urgently. Hence the
change of posting for Ernest Walton.

They were ordered to visit Erigavo on 14th June, Bereba on 17th
June, and Boroma on 19th June. The task of the RMO was to
medically examine each recruit 'in accordance with the PULHEEMS
system, as far as is practicable.'

They left on the 9th of June, under command of Major Clarke.
He commanded the training depot, hence his role as recruiter. 'He
and his wife were delightful people, the nicest British family I met.
We set out after breakfast for a 125 mile drive eastwards through the
bush. My vehicle was full, with the Clarkes in the cab and behind

heir three servants, my boy Dahir, an armed escort of two soldiers, ne standing on a sort of platform behind the cab, and about half a on of kit. The country seemed almost uninhabited, with almost no raffic and only an occasional cluster of native huts with nearby erds of sheep and goats, and only two trucks and one camel train during the whole day.

'At night, after darkness fell, as always suddenly at 6.15 to 6.30, we had a comfortable meal – hot tinned stew, followed by fruit salad, also tinned. After, we sat and chatted for awhile before retiring. The African night was sheer magic – I wrote, "sitting out in the bush in the romantic silence of a deep tropical night, with on one hand the Pole Star to the north, and on the other, just above the horizon to the south, the Southern Cross, is a very fine way of passing time."

'Next day we were off at 7 a.m. after a breakfast of cereal and bread, and after a similar day except that we spent a few hours crossing a bleak windswept landscape which, if there had been heather, would have reminded one of Scotland . . . and so to Erigavo in the late afternoon where hundreds of nomads, warned in advance by the "bush telegraph" had gathered to meet us.

'Afternoon tea with the Somali Medical Assistant who had a rather nice bungalow, and then we stayed overnight in an adjacent bungalow which was used by the District Commissioner on his visits. Next day we spent recruiting – Major Clarke and a senior Somali sergeant picked out a number of men from each tribal group, according to pre-determined formula to keep a proper balance in the numbers of each tribe – Gadabursi, Wasengaili, Dolbahunta and Isahaq, although for some reason I did not understand, there were never enough Ishaq (the most warlike tribe, apparently feared by the others) – more than one hundred in all. I was under strict instructions to reject anybody with even the slightest abnormality, but nearly all the men were in good shape, though all were very slim.

'Next after exploring Erigavo – it consisted of a small cluster of European-style bungalows, a police post, post office, and a small hospital, where I looked at a few ill people for the medical assistant – there was no doctor – once a month the doctor from Burao called, and the native quarter – an Indian shop, a coffee shop, a white rectangular mosque with a small minaret, and one or two windowless houses. Next day on to Hargeisa, to examine the men recruited by the colonel . . . then to Boroma in the far west of the country at about 5000 feet. There were two National Service subalterns there and I stayed with them. It was the site of the training unit where the raw recruits were turned into soldiers by Somali instructors under the guidance of Major Clarke . . . here rolling meadows with grass and even an occasional field of maize or millet and gentle hills and valleys. When my work there was done, it was back to Burao to start my proper job.'

North were Palestine and Ethiopia. In the earliest years of conscription, troops were active in Palestine during the troubles which Jewish terrorist groups created. Tom Richards was RMO with 41st Field Regiment, RA, from 1947. The regiment had to rush to Haifa to prevent unloading of illegal immigrants, and to assist the Palestine police. After his first year, he was sent to join a Military Mission to Ethiopia. He was six months in Dessye, with six other officers and the mission advised the Ethiopian Army during its manoeuvres. His responsibilities were for units spread over some 500 miles, and followed the usual lines of sick care, medical inspections, but also lectures, given with the help of an interpreter. Back in Addis Ababa, he had the responsible task of ordering drugs and medical supplies for the local military.

South of Kenya was Rhodesia (Zimbabwe). Flight Lieutenant Ken Spittlehouse was on RAF course no.135 at Moreton in Marsh after graduating from Sheffield in 1949. He was assigned to the Headquarters unit of the Rhodesian Air Training Group at Kumalo, Bulawayo, Southern Rhodesia (now Zimbabwe). 'I had never been abroad before and had some trepidation' he recalled, 'but I needn't have worried.'

'The great adventure began on 19th January, 1950, when we embarked on the Union Castle Royal Mail Motor Vessel *Stirling Castle* at Southampton. There were five other officers as well as a number of other ranks. Although the ship had its own surgeon, the

1ealth of the RAF personnel was my responsibility. Shortly after
leaving Funchal in Madeira, I was summoned to the bridge where a
very irate captain instructed me to see to one of the airmen who had
gone berserk. He had totally wrecked his cabin and was deeply
unconscious . . . with help I got him round . . . all his bottles were
confiscated.

'I quickly learned a great deal about RAF life from my fellow
officers who were all regulars and several years older than myself.
Most had seen war service and to my eyes were very worldly wise.
One marvellous aspect of the voyage was the food. Britain was still
experiencing rationing so the menus were staggering by their
diversity and we enjoyed our meals enormously. We disembarked at
Capetown on February 3rd, 1950.

'We went by train to Bulawayo. This was a tedious journey of
1600 miles. The heat on the train was unbearable and the food poor,
especially compared to that on the voyage . . . However we
eventually reached Bulawayo early Sunday morning having been on
the train for three days and four nights. We were met at the station
by some of the members of the Kumalo Officers' Mess and taken to
the camp, approximately three miles outside Bulawayo. As a special
concession the bar was opened and an alcoholic breakfast was
enjoyed by all present. I was allocated my own quarters on the
station, being the only one of the group who would be permanently
based at Kumalo, all the others moving to one of the other two
other RAF stations, Thornhill (Navigation Training School) and
Heany (Flying Training School).

As the MO whom he was replacing had a little time to serve
before going home, Ken was sent for a short attachment to Heany.
There he met Flight Lieutenant Gordon Ewan; they became life-
long friends.

On the way back to Kumalo to take up his duties, his driver
decided to race a railway train to a level crossing. 'He made it to the
crossing, but then managed to stall the engine on the track with the
heavy freight train some 50 yards from us. The impact sent the truck
flying, we made several revolutions and I went through the open
window whilst the driver clung desperately to the steering wheel.
Fortunately the impact pushed the vehicle to one side of the track

and I was at the edge of the rails when the train passed by. The train eventually stopped, having cleared the crossing and the crew came running back expecting to find two mangled bodies. I had lost most of the skin from my back as well as sustaining an extensive laceration on the crown of my head. The driver had no injuries whatsoever. As traffic on the road was very light, we had to wait quite a long time before anyone appeared. Eventually we made it back to Heany, where Gordon Ewen repaired my scalp and applied dressings to my back.' He was given some leave to recover; the driver was court marshalled.

His medical duties at Kumalo were to look after the airmen and their families. There were also men from the Rhodesian African Regiment, (RAR) who did guard duties and acted as orderlies and batmen; they too had their families as patients. There was the standard small hospital.

Like others of us, he had seen little or no infectious diseases of children. Here his saviour was the wife of a Warrant Officer amongst his patients – she had quite a large family. She happily demonstrated typical cases of measles, German measles, chicken pox, as and when they occurred, to the new MO general practitioner! On the other hand, his training in tropical disease when doing his basic training stood him in good stead. Malaria, amoebic dysentery, and bilharzia were common among the native population. Some RAF became ill with malaria and dysentery, but none with bilharzia – the water regulations were rigidly enforced. Swimming in open waters was forbidden, and all water where swimming was allowed was heavily treated.'

He had the typical life of the National Service doctor – his home visits were done at first in ambulances (which was unusual) – 'to say they had seen better days would be an understatement. The Ford V8 had originally, according to a plaque on its dashboard, seen service in the Middle East in 1942. Apart from being an uncomfortable ride it had several idiosyncrasies. When negotiating a right turn the driver's door had a tendency to fly open, whilst the gear lever tended to disengage. To combat these tendencies, it was advisable to steer with the right hand while holding on to the door with the left hand and simultaneously jamming one's left knee hard on the gear lever to stop it jumping out. One became quite adept at these practices, but it did take a bit of practice. Later the officer in charge of the MT section took pity on me, and gave me a Ford V8 saloon.'

He enjoyed his flying. The pilots offered him trips, took him on night flying exercises, showed him their skill in aerobatics, and in spite of some, he told proudly that he was never air sick. Several trips were made to the Victoria Falls. Training flights took him over large parts of Southern Rhodesia – 'sometimes we had the excitement of flying *under* the bridges which crossed the Zambesi and other rivers – strictly against regulations, of course!' Once he flew to Johannesburg with a patient with a suspected brain tumour.

Life in RAF messes was comfortable and enjoyable, and his was no exception. They once entertained Sir Geoffrey Huggins, Prime Minister of Rhodesia, in their mess, when he had a large share in the organizing. Ken shared a quarter with the Church of England padre, Rev Tom Robinson. They enjoyed each other's company. Horse riding and tennis and a little golf were his recreations – he purchased his own horse, Nimbus.

In January 1951 Wing Commander Guy Robinson, the Group Accountant Officer, invited him to join him on a trip to Capetown, where he was to meet his sister who was coming to Rhodesia for a holiday. 'He had just taken delivery of a new Humber Hawk, which had been shipped from the UK, and at that time, was the height of luxury in motor vehicles. The trip was to take us down through South Africa, on the main highway, the N1, to Johannesburg and Capetown. We were then to travel back to Bulawayo via Port Elizabeth.

'It was a memorable trip with a first night stop at a small hotel in Bechuanaland (Botswana). During the night a thief crept into my room while I was sleeping, and robbed me of clothes and money. Not an auspicious start.

'The journey continued to Johannesburg, crossing into South Africa at Biet Bridge, over the Limpopo River. Guy had friends in Johannesburg, one of whom was the secretary of the Glendower Golf Club. We stayed a few days playing a game or two of golf and attended the local races. Another of Guy's friends was a horse trainer. From there we travelled down through South Africa, passing through Bloemfontein, Beaufort West, and Worcester before reaching Capetown. Driving down through the Great Karoo desert was an experience. The road is as straight an arrow for mile after mile, with only an occasional vehicle.

'It was a spectacular descent into the Western Cape from the high plateau, on which a fair proportion of South Africa perches, through the Toitskloof Pass. A descent that was a bit hairy at times. Off the plateau it was glorious to behold the large orchards and green fields, which are, or were then, so much a part of the Western Cape.' Ken Spittelhouse's account sounds as if his was one of the most pleasant National Service experience as could be imagined.

Lieutenant David Parsons, brought up in Ebbw Vale, and a graduate of St Andrews, had a less smooth opening to his Service. At home, he had got his wish to go to central Africa by the toss of a coin. His posting in December 1958 was to be RMO to 2 KAR (King's African Rifles), Central Africa Federal Forces, HQ, Zomba, Nyasaland (Malawi) via Nairobi. 'A further attraction was an extra allowance paid by all these overseas armies to those on secondment, and they did not differentiate between regular and NS personnel. 'So I was off on a 21 month tour of central Africa and being paid extra for going. I could not believe my luck.'

But on his arrival at Nairobi, after a less-than-smooth journey, he reported to the RTO (rail transport officer). The major told him to take a plane immediately to Lusaka, Northern Rhodesia. 'I refused. He responded: "you cannot refuse my order, you nasty little NS man (or similar)." "My posting, Sir, is to 2 KAR, in Zomba, and I am not going to Lusaka!" The major replied: "They are in Lusaka!" I replied: "They are in Zomba, and I am not going to Lusaka!"' Eventually the RTO agreed that he could stay until the whereabouts of 2 KAR was determined. All was well; he got to Zomba.

He commented: 'In those days of the Cold War, all sub-Sahara countries were colonies except Rhodesia, a semi-Independent Crown Colony, and South Africa, a Commonwealth Dominion. In the event of WW3, all their forces were grouped together under the command of UK Forces HQ, Nairobi. In December 1958, HQ Nairobi did not know where its forces were positioned. I and 2

KAR had rotated between Lusaka and Zomba six months earlier; Whitehall and Salisbury (Harare) knew, but neither had informed Nairobi.'

'On 12th December, with tickets from the RTO, I boarded an East Africa Airways Dakota for Mombasa and places south. After Mombasa we passed Kilimanjaro *en route* to Tanga, Pemba, Zanzibar, Dar es Salaam and finally, in the evening, to Blantyre, Nyasaland. A colonial backwater to most people, Nyasaland was not entirely unknown to me, for I had read recently *Venture into The Interior* by Laurens van de Post. After Nairobi with its avenues, modern hotel (one) and electricity, here was primitive Africa. The mess and all the accommodation were lathe and wattle with straw roofs. Lighting and all the fridges were powered by paraffin. Cooking was on wood stoves. Big game, (he later went on a lion hunt) although diminishing, was still around.

'The officers' quarters were on the lower slope of Mt. Zomba and looked across Palombe Plain to the massive Mt Mlanje 40 miles away. The first morning I was struck by the similarity with the view of the Cuillin Hills across the water from Elgol in Skye. I had cycled there from Dundee in 1952, to see them.'

He had the same duties and range of responsibilities, the same time table, as all other RMOs. His batman he regarded as a real scrounger, but Damion scrounged on his account, and could always produce a cup of tea, wherever they were or whatever the circumstances. He had the support of the local small civil hospital. His unit had a traditional Christmas, listened to the Queen's speech, and on Boxing Day, a traditional football match between officers and NCOs.

Lieutenant Parsons discovered he had a potential money problem. He found he was earning a quarter of equivalent ranks in the officers' mess. He had transferred money from home, but saw he could well become short. 'My money came from a UK/ Rhodesia military liaison office in Salisbury with whom I entered an acrimonious correspondence with War Office about the Rhodesia allowance I was promised when I volunteered. They knew nothing of this allowance, saying it did not exist. I protested but was told to shut up or face disciplinary action. I shut up. However, I learned that the Director General, RAMC, was to visit Salisbury in February, so I requested an interview.

'Coming out of the Rhodesia RAMC DG's office he gave me the bum's rush, never enquiring why I wished to see him. I knew he knew but to the Regular Army Nat Serv. Men were just a pain in the proverbial. I flew back to Zomba empty handed, and despondent knowing I was going to have trouble with my bills.'

All was taken care of, however, when the political situation deteriorated, rioting started all over Nyasaland, and a State of Emergency was declared, banning all public assemblies of more than six people. Those who had been in Kenya with its Mau Mau terror were worried that the same was going to happen there. He was issued with a 9mm revolver, and told to shoot as necessary. Suddenly the Army was sent out to guard installations all over Nyasaland, the RRAF flew sorties, and Rhodesia moved in reserve and regular battalions. He had a personal confrontation with an angry crowd while on the way from Blantyre to Zomba, had a frightening few minutes when it looked likely that the crowd would attack, but dealt with the incident by facing the biggest man in the front row of the crowd. Then he suddenly remembered that his revolver was not loaded. He walked back to his car, turned away from the crowd to load it, remembering what he had been taught at Aldershot in how to load a firearm, and found to his alarm that he had been issued with rimless ammunition, which did not fit! Luckily an armed riot squad came on the scene, the crowd fled, and all was well.

His fear of financial problems was happily resolved. Although the RAMC had not had the grace to help in any way, and he had the all-too-usual bullying so characteristic of the British Army, his own Commanding Officer came to his aid when he discovered he was paid so much less than the regiment's own officers. 'Signals were sent to Army HQ in Salisbury, and very shortly afterwards a Bill was rushed through the Rhodesian Parliament inaugurating the Rhodesian Allowance to make up the pay of seconded personnel to their local equivalents. Suddenly I was earning more than I would have as a regular in the British Army. In September 1959 I was automatically made up to Captain with further jumps in basic pay and Rhodesia Allowance. This was a local allowance so it was not classed as income, and because it was paid directly by the Rhodesians and not through the British Army, it was not taxed. The result was that my net pay was now higher than that of the Rhodesians.'

West Africa was similar in most ways. The accounts by our NS colleagues depended, as on the other side, upon the date when they did their service. Those who served earlier saw less political activity, just as on the eastern side.

John Tallack, an Aberdeen graduate, came early, in 1949. He was to be RMO to the 1st Battalion, Gold Coast Regiment, at Tamale in the Northern Territories of the Gold Coast (Ghana). His flight in a tiny ten seat two-engined aeroplane was disturbing – the cheery pilot plunged the plane down and upwards. 'My queasy feelings made worse by the breath of the passenger in the seat behind me, a Lebanese merchant who appeared to have never eaten anything except garlic.

'Tamale proved to be a primitive village of mudhuts, with dirt roads and tracks. My living quarters were a round thatched mud hut, with a metal framed bed, an upright wooden chair, a wooden table, and outside washing set with a basin and ewer, and a "thunder box" with its shovel for wood shavings. A batman was attached to me, who would attend to my clothing and other requirements, and he lost no time in telling me that he would need money to go to market to buy a charcoal iron, charcoal, scrubbing soap, starch, polish, Brasso and so on. The next day he came in accompanied by a tall, beautiful naked girl, saying "This be my sister, Master." Not knowing what else to do I said: 'How do you do?" "Do you want to buy her?" the batman said. "Not at present, thank you very much" was all I could think of to say.'

'I became rapidly aware that I was very lucky to be part of a colonial lifestyle soon to disappear. We dressed for dinner, ran flags up and down to celebrate many battles, birthdays, Empire Day, and on all sorts of occasions. Many of the civilian Europeans had been all their life in the Indian Colonial Service and we were part of the civil population as well as the military. Many of the members of the mess played polo – there was a very active polo club in Tamale.'

His own medical establishment followed the usual lines – half a mile away from the mess, a senior African sergeant who ran the place, a consulting room, a dispensary, a laboratory, and a 20-bedded ward. His African staff were competent to do routine nursing; in addition he had two RAMC corporals who did all the urine testing, stool testing, and looked at blood films for malarial parasites. As the new doctor, he had to learn himself how to test and diagnose, to draw out guinea worm from the skin by rolling it round a match stick, patiently day by day. He saw a child die of rabies three hours after being brought in by his mother; terrible sepsis among some Africans. He too went on a recruiting drive, spending a week north of Tamale examining new recruits. He met and admired the dedicated colonial senior civil surgeon, who, like others in Africa, did a large range of major surgery because there was no-one else to do it. Similarly he learned from the local physician; he benefited by all their great experience and authority. As a result, he had none of the criticism his compatriots in Germany had of senior but much less capable Regular RAMC. When he had to do his monthly indents, he learned the necessity of allowing his sergeant to dictate the requirements, or to just order what had been ordered the previous month. 'I started to have the first inklings of the extent of wastage in the Forces,' he mused.

He bought a new 1949 Standard Vanguard car, which was to allow him to see much more of the Gold Coast than would otherwise have been possible. The Gold Coast was part of the export market, and so he could buy his car for £430 instead of £650 as at home.

After six months, he was moved to the Regiment's Recruiting and Training Centre in Kumasi, in Ashanti. This was quite a different climate and vegetation. It was a little cooler, but more humid. 'I had a large bungalow with a garden, at the bottom of which was a house in which my batman lived with his wife and children. The Officers' Mess was a superb building reminiscent of a French Chateau, built on stilts, with graceful steps winding up on each side. The interior was large and gracious – a dining room, an ante room, and a full-sized billiard room. There was a stupe – a balcony with an apron shaped extension at the entrance, with easy chairs. In Kumasi the

European community was much larger. On arrival I had to go to the District Commissioner's residence, sign his book, and in due course would be invited to a Sunday lunch – a function hosted by the DC and his wife every Sunday. The lunch was certainly hospitality to a formula. (When John arrived, his predecessor, John Phillips, took him immediately to his tailor). The civil administration was very efficient, and I got to know people from all departments; Police, Public Works, Education, Forestry – and many commercial enterprises, notably the UAC (United Africa Company), with branches in every village selling everything from suit lengths to sacks of coal, and the UTC (United Trading Company), a French owned enterprise of similar universality.'

His predecessor, Captain Phillips, had grown so fond of Kumasi that he had decided to take his discharge locally, and stay to set up general practice in the town. He had already built a practice, and wished to do all he could for women patients. From John Tallack's account, Dr Phillips was a dedicated doctor with the future of the Africans very much at heart.

Tom Begg from Glasgow served his two years in the Gold Coast also, but in Takoradi with the 1st Gold Coast Regiment, and from 1951-53. The amount of responsibility given him amazed him, in his subsequent career a first-class consultant physician. 'I cannot imagine any doctor now being regarded as mature enough to do what I was called upon to do,' he remembered. His Corporal Quainoo would arrive with labouring women in trouble, and he was obstetrician as well as RMO.

He had the usual ample time for sport. He had been Scottish half mile champion, but in spite of hard training, could not manage to beat Sanni Thomas, the Gold Coast champion, when he ran for the Army against him. He also played tennis and hockey, and for additional recreation, drove around on his motor bicycle. Together with the adjutant, the dental officer, Ronnie Pearson who later became Director General of the Dental Services, he travelled around, going as far as Accra. Poisonous snakes on the routes were a hazard.

Just a little later came John Billinghurst to the Gold Coast, from

1954 to 1955. He however was at 37th General Military Hospital in Accra. He was a GDMO, but with special responsibility for families. The hospital was on the outskirts of Accra. It consisted of 'numerous single-storey buildings of a rather nondescript character.' Accra was the location of the HQ of all the Forces in British West Africa, and the military hospital was correspondingly important. It had some link with the large government hospital at Korle Bu, five miles away. He found the staff from all over the United Kingdom. 'Our physician was a friendly Irishman, Major Lyons. The commanding officer was a lively Welshman, Lieut-Colonel "Dicky Richards", whom the National Servicemen who made up the rest of the staff liked because of his interest in clinical medicine. The surgeon was another Irishman, Dudley Staunton, later a consultant at St Bartholomew's Hospital in London, the pathologist a likeable Englishman, John Hunt, as was the anaesthetist and ophthalmologist, Michael Raynor.' In the wards were the QARANC sisters, with locally enlisted nurses and orderlies.

'The southern half of the Gold Coast held the largest proportion of well educated Africans of any colony and most of the men could speak English remarkably well. The vast majority of medical orderlies, secretaries, technicians, and truck drivers were friendly and eager to talk to you – some of their English was of the form immortalized by Gerald Durrell's books about catching animals in the Cameroons, and sometimes delightfully quaint. For example, menstrual periods were called flowers. A Gold Coaster who had received further education in Britain or America was described as a been-to, and a female equivalent was a been-tress.

'The main area of recruitment for non-skilled soldiers was in the Northern Territories of the country, amongst illiterates who were profoundly despised by the southerners. Nevertheless, it was from those parts of the country that many of the longest serving men came, men who had served in Burma in the famous 81st Division. Such men could rise to the highest ranks among the non-commissioned officers, but not beyond. There were a few, a very few, Ghanaian commissioned officers, the most senior being Captain Arthur Ankrah, destined in later years to become a President of the country.'

His day routine was as all the rest, except perhaps that breakfast was always a traditional English one of bacon and eggs. There were enough of the medical officers to allow plenty of time off if not OMO (Orderly Medical Officer). In the afternoons 'we could have a siesta or arrange to go in an army truck to the local beach at Labadi.

'Labadi was a dream world – a sandy palm-fringed beach looking out to magnificent Atlantic rollers which were ideal for surfing. But danger lurked in the form of strong under-tows and side currents, so army beach pickets with whistles were always on duty, one by each of two red flags on the beach, and transgressing beyond the line of the flags or beyond the start of the breakers was strictly forbidden.

'For part of the time one of my tasks was to lecture on army health to officer cadets at the Command Training Centre at Teshi, near Accra. If the cadets were considered good enough they were sent on to Sandhurst. Two of the cadets became lifelong friends of mine. One was Philemon Quaye, destined to become Commodore in the Ghanaian Navy and then Ghana's Ambassador in Cairo. He was a man of profound honour and integrity. The other was Yakubu Gowon, a future President of Nigeria. Yakubu came from a small tribe, the Angas, located in the Middle Belt of Nigeria, on the Jos Peninsula. Like Philemon, he was a committed Christian. He had the most extraordinarily attractive personality, reliable, free of guile, eager to make friends with everyone he met, affectionate, and seemingly never taking offence. He was so much liked at Sandhurst that he was voted Cadet of the Year. He spent a Christmas at the home of my parents, who were as enchanted with him as were all his other acquaintances, and felt that with men like that the future of Africa was bright indeed. He was also a guest at our wedding. Later, during the Biafran war, he was wrongly accused of tribal hatreds, the exact opposite was in fact the case, for he strove consistently to promote the conviction that the Ibos were fellow-Nigerians and should be welcomed back into the family. Admittedly many of them died, but from disease and starvation rather than tribal massacres.

'There was no reason whatever for any of us in the Army to get involved in local politics, but it was of course an intensely interesting time as the Gold Coast was quite clearly going to be the first African colony to achieve independence. The Governor was Sir Charles

Arden-Clark, a brilliant choice. He was thought to hold left-wing views, though they would hardly be considered left of centre nowadays. More important was the skill with which he related to and manoeuvred with Dr Kwame Nkrumah, the upstart politician back from his studies in the United States, who had displaced the venerable Dr Danquah as the likely First Minister of Ghana. When the day for hand-over arrived, everything was carried out with the maximum of goodwill and friendliness, setting the tone for all the English-speaking African colonies and protectorates.'

Another 'early' doctor was Lieutenant John Reid. He was in Sierra Leone from 1950 till 1952, at the small military hospital of 30 beds in Freetown. Here he saw and treated the diseases prevalent – chronic malaria, kwashiorkor, a disease due to poor nutrition, constant venereal disease in the Africans, and bilharzia. It came as a surprise to see so much chickenpox. He saw much tuberculosis, and one of his NS colleagues had to be invalided home urgently with this disease. The military hospital had no X-ray facility, so patients needing X-Ray had to be sent to the local civilian Colonial Medical Service one.

He had two spells of duty outside Freetown. One was to a very small outpost called Daru, and the second was to Gambia. Here he helped Dr McGregor of the MRC (Medical Research Council) unit which was carrying out field work on malaria, 'the Greatest Disease in the World.' The team were studying the life cycle of the mosquito, trying to find possible means of preventing it acting as a vector of the disease.

Like all others, he and his colleagues enjoyed playing games in the cooler afternoons, swimming from the lovely beach on half days, and they all smoked. 'With cigarettes at 20 pence for a tin of 50,' he wrote in his memoir, 'little encouragement was required for most of us to become smokers! This was in the 1950s, before Doll and Hill had published their preliminary report.'

Nigeria was a major military area. Lieutenant David Boyd graduated from Edinburgh in 1950. In due course he too would become an outstanding consultant physician there. Like the large majority of those of the early 1950s, he was not anti-National Service: 'We were very conscious of the privilege of being able to train during the war years. We looked forward to new experience.' Like the majority of his compatriots, too, he was conscious that 'some in the Regular RAMC as being there because they would have had difficulty in making their way in civilian life.' He saw at once the gulf between the regulars and his own clinical teachers, and the really able medical men in the big world outside the Army. He was happy with his posting to West Africa, and found Lieut-Colonel Meneces helpful with advice.

After the shock of being told that he was to be 'Officer Commanding plane', he enjoyed an excellent lunch at Bordeaux *en route*, and he, too, marvelled at the vastness of the Sahara desert. He was bound for the military hospital at Lagos. There he found the clinical work fascinating, both the exotic illnesses and those he already knew about from his house training in Edinburgh. During his time he enjoyed moves to Kaduna, to the 4th Battalion, Nigeria Regiment at Enugu in the south east. On the railway journey back to Kaduna again, he had to deliver a 'piccan' (an African baby) while the train stopped on the bridge over the River Niger at Jebba.

He experienced two very different VIP visits. 'There was a visit from General Cantlie, who was I think DGAMS at the time. I was appointed officer in charge of the parade and inspection of the hospital and staff. We practised for weeks and eventually got good at a simple march on to the parade, inspection, and march off, led by the military band of the 3rd Nigerian Regiment, whom we borrowed for the occasion. All went well and I was leading my troops away, when the CSM dashed up saying the general wished to address his troops and wanted me to form a hollow square! Chaos ensued. It may be that I was the last British officer on the continent of Africa – or anywhere – to be ordered to form a hollow square.'

The other visit was the reverse of the pomposity of the Director General's. 'Edwina, Countess Mountbatten of Burma, visited in her Red Cross role. At this time the CO was a Colonel Mathieson, an Aberdeen graduate, and we had a very relaxed and pleasant time with a memorable lunch in the Sisters' Mess. She insisted in seeing every man, including the VD ward. One of my orderlies had been in

Burma and wore the Burma ribbon. "Ah" she said, "I see you were in Burma with my husband." What a beam of pride spread over that African face!'

'Nigeria looks flat' said Alastair Simmons, a graduate from St Andrews. He had been a Harkness scholar there. He too had asked for a posting to Africa, being well aware that this was an opportunity not to be missed. His time was spent mainly at Kaduna. 'Here it was about 1500 feet up. The heat was over 100°F all the time, but it was all right as it was dry. In Lagos, it was 80°F but the humidity was 80 as well. Most of the year it was desert. But in the later part of the year, as the rains fell, the grass would grow about a foot a day – you went out in the morning and by nightfall it was a foot higher. Then they burnt the often 20 feet high grass – the bush fires were striking. Although it was desert, there were white Kapok flowers and blood-red plants called "flamboyant" – they were beautiful.

'I worked in the lab as I was going to do bacteriology, and the experience I got stood me in good stead – all that parasitology – and later I was the expert at home when there was any question of parasitic infection. The general duty I had to do I enjoyed . . . you saw so very many ill people, many Africans you were able to help, and it gave you a sense of fulfilment I never had in quite the same way again. Once the CO took me to the District Commissioner's House so that I could inoculate him and his family – he hadn't done anything like that for a long time and wanted another doctor to do it. The CO, Colonel McNeil, was mad keen on hockey. Although he was quite old, he played every day and he made us play it.' (John Billinghurst told the same story. 'We had to play against local civilian teams – one of Irish priests who played hurley were devils on the hockey pitch.')

At times mentally disturbed Africans were brought in to the BMH. Alastair recalled one truck arriving, with a maniacal woman inside. 'The orderlies opened the cover, and there she was, shouting and violent. I was pushed inside. In a flash, I found all the African orderlies had vanished and I was alone in the back of the truck about to be attacked and in fear of my life.'

'The British were aware that when we left there was going to be big trouble between the two parts of the country', he recalled. 'They arranged a big military exercise. There were five battalions, 5 to 10,000 troops in total, with only about 300 white officers and NCOs. We went to the Jos plateau – now that is the high part in the north, about 4000 feet. It is the mountainous part – you can look south and wonder at the blood red sunsets, and see for miles down the incline towards the south. We had to march south towards Kano, the big town of a million inhabitants, to evacuate Hausas to the north. On the way, I was once scared a baboon was going to attack me. I had the wonderful experience of sleeping under my mosquito net, under the stars, as we were out on exercise. There were plenty of real casualties.'

Alastair Simmons was another who found his time in West Africa something he never forgot, and like David Boyd, he looked back on it with affection. In due course he achieved his ambition to become a bacteriologist; his Rutherford Gold Medal MD at St Andrews, on 'The polysaccharides of the Genus Shigella' was judged to have been the finest St Andrews MD thesis of the twentieth century.

Philip Smith went to the Cameroons a decade later. He was called up on 26th September, 1960, so he was one of the very last National Servicemen. As he had taken his FRCS, he was posted as surgeon to 50 FST (Field Surgical Team) to the British Cameroons. 'I went on embarkation leave thinking that the British Cameroons must be somewhere near the Cameron Highlands in Malaya. The atlas I consulted soon made it clear I was going to West Africa. At that time there was to be a plebiscite and the inhabitants of the British Cameroons (originally a German colony until the end of the First War) had to decide whether to join Nigeria or the Cameroon Republic. 1400 troops were there to see fair play.'

He flew by way of Tripoli, where replacements were required, Kano in Nigeria, and after an overnight, to the base camp at Buea. 'I found it especially hot as I had UK battledress but no tropical equipment whatsoever. At Busea I was kitted out, met the CO, and was invited to get on with things.'

He had the same pleasant time – learned to surf, water-ski, play golf and have dinner with the Governor. 'The local ex-patriate civilian population was also very hospitable, introducing me to brandy and ginger, golf and water-skiing.'

And as with the others, he had the inestimable aid from the local civilian medical doctors. Like his compatriots, he respected the skill and dedication of these hard-working men. His work was surgery. 'I found it possible to do operating lists most weeks if the cases were relatively minor, e.g. hernias when I gave my own spinal anaesthetics. On these lists we dealt with many acute cases admitted. Here a general anaesthetic was frequently needed and was given by one of two young nurses who were going as Baptist missionaries to the Congo, but whose destination had been changed because of the war going on there at that time. General anaesthesia involved pentothal after which the surgeon cleaned and towelled the patient, thumping his chest and pressing on it if he did not breathe immediately; alternatively the incision would be made which acted as an effective stimulant. Further pentothal was given as required, there was no other anaesthetic agent. If there was a major operation such as a thyroidectomy, we called in the consultant anaesthetist.'

He can summarize the feelings of this chapter's contributors: 'When I joined the Army in September 1960 I had no particular enthusiasm for what appeared to be an unnecessary break in the development of my surgical training. By 1962 however, I had reason to be immensely grateful for the experiences which had broadened my mind and changed my life in ways that I would never have predicted.'

CHAPTER VIII

Malaya

MALAYA WAS A major theatre in the National Service Era. The garrison was enormous, Army, with the incomparable Gurkhas, and Royal Air Force. Reports were of two main kinds – from those whose activities were in units fighting the terrorists, and from those who were predominately in the larger military hospitals. More reminiscences came from this theatre than from any other one.

Lieutenant Alan Reay, a National Serviceman who progressed to become Director General of the Army Medical Services, described the political background.

'During the Second World War, the Chinese resistance groups functioning inside the Malay jungles after the fall of Singapore were believed to have accepted assistance from the British with reluctance. They did so only to help what they saw as the temporary problem of the Japanese occupation. Their real objective was to establish a communist Malayan State, dominated by them, the Chinese. They resented the British "Imperialists" particularly because of our apparent policy in the early 1940s of training the Malay, and to an extent the Indian, population, but *not* the Chinese population, who had immigrated in large numbers since the 1870s as labourers in mines and elsewhere. Spencer Chapman, in his book *The Jungle is Neutral*, mentioned that a small number of Indians, but very few Malays, eventually joined the guerrilla groups in the jungle. From mid-August 1945, all guerrillas were paid 30 dollars a month by the British Army and issued with "34 Corps" shoulder flashes to wear. Despite this gesture, within less than three years, Chinese guerrilla leaders such as Chen Ping (who had been important allies in Spencer Chapman's endeavours in the jungle), became our leading enemies in the long Malayan campaign fought by Britain against what had now become the Chinese terrorists.'

The terrorist campaign was just beginning when Lieutenant

George Watts from Birmingham arrived to begin his service, early in 1947. His initial experience was not as happy as many. He was perplexed at the curious way postings were allocated – at the Depot it seemed as if they were just done alphabetically, except for those who had a games skill. 'I had entered for my final FRCS examination in surgery and my thesis for a mastership in surgery had been accepted. I therefore asked whether I would be able to sit the exams and take up my mastership as it appeared to me that with them I should be better qualified to serve the Army's purpose. I was assured that there was no problem as far as this was concerned. This proved to be a total lie. On the days of the two events I was aboard a troopship bound for the Far East.' When he set off, he found all his clothing and baggage totally unsuitable, and then that no arrangements had been made to transfer him from the railway station in Liverpool to the ship.

'We were none too pleased when we found there were twelve officers in a cabin which in normal times would have taken two third class passengers, until later when we discovered the conditions under which the other ranks were accommodated. I found two eighteen year old boys who slept alongside the propeller shaft of the ship. The noise was gross and in the event of mishap, they would have been doomed. One could not but be reminded of Kipling's poem "Tommy this and Tommy that etc". There seemed to be little thought given to the welfare of the British Other Ranks. The only medical care was for FFI (freedom from infection) checks to see if they were free from lice. This was carried out in a coarse and unfeeling, public, fashion. Only on one occasion did we see the ship's surgeon. This was when a man was found to have an abscess. The other medical passenger was an anaesthetist – a man later to become known as one of the leaders of his speciality. We were asked to open it.'

With his anaesthetist colleague he was moved at once to a transit camp called Nee Soon. Here they discovered that they were not needed as it had been an oversight to request a surgical team. They were separated, and George was sent to a joint British-Indian unit in the hospital at Johore Bahru. Here he worked hard with an Indian surgical colleague, admired the Anglo-Indian Commanding Officer,

espected the excellent nursing staff, managed to get himself tropical
it – made in two days by a local tailor, and was settling down when
ll the Indian medical and nursing orderlies left suddenly to return
ome to India! Indian independence had been granted!

'In my first few weeks I encountered military paper work for the
irst time. As the surgeon, I had to provide the quarterly records of
he unit's surgical activity. I assiduously collected all the records and
luly submitted my report, which was sent to headquarters at Base.
t was returned at once with a crisp note that it was grossly
naccurate. Infuriated, I consulted the CO. His advice was simple.
Copy out the last report and alter it a little. Then send it back. I did
o and it was accepted. On such data are armies managed!

'The quartermaster to the unit, a promoted regular army
quartermaster-sergeant, seemed to be able to live better than us in
nore ways than one. When the new CO arrived, after the Anglo-
ndian Commander had left, he and the quartermaster dissociated
hemselves from the rest of us, the National Service officers,
specially as we were all non-smokers and even though alcohol was
heap, non-drinking. A rift slowly, albeit silently, developed between
s and them.

'I personally was not affected, as I had established contact with
he nearby native hospital and its surgeon. For a time we were
imited there in what we were able to do, as we had no trained
naesthetist. When one arrived, an enthusiastic man, we were able to
elp the local population once more. In that area there was a very
igh incidence of cleft palate and hare lip, for which no treatment
ad been available. Having had quite a large experience of this I
pproached the local REME unit to make some suitable
nstruments. They showed great enterprise and cleverness, and made
s a variety of instruments from a variety of oddments. The REME
vere great. Intravenous therapy in infants was difficult as we had no
mall cannulae, but together we managed to create some, which
llowed us to give bone marrow transfusions of home made saline.
Then after a few weeks, the new CO decided he could not allow
oth the anaesthetist and me to be away at the same time. We
ontinued to do our best to help the local people, but our disap-
ointment was extreme.'

The juniors watched with admiration how a newly arrived and extremely beautiful Red Cross girl set about caring for the collection of orphan children living in the camp area whose parents had been murdered by the Japanese. The medical officers were told to set up education for their NS soldiers, but when they sent for a collection of suitable books, only one arrived, and that written in the 1930s. The same applied to paints the young officers asked for; when these arrived, they were so old and hard that no one could use them. The young men who had shown interest in painting local things were disappointed. There is little doubt that there was a desire of many of the young soldiers to learn about local people and their customs and it was frustrating that so little help was actually given.

As terrorist activity began, war casualties arrived. George Watts as the surgeon established an ADS (Advanced Dressing Station) in one of the old colonial houses at a place called Kuala Kanga. 'On the whole', he reminisced, 'these only occurred when our troops went out to search for bandits. The main victims of the guerrillas were the native population who were forced to serve them and hide them in the small villages and small clearings they had made in the jungle in attempts to make a life for themselves as farmers. Gathering the wounded was not always easy. Sometimes we brought them by road, but we were also able to use Artillery spotting planes. These were small flimsy aircraft whose main wing span resembled a piece of bicycle frame. To transport a wounded man we strapped him on a stretcher, removed the two cockpit windows and then strapped the stretcher along the fuselage with his head in the cockpit and his feet towards the tail. The skill of those pilots always impressed me. I was always afraid.

'At other times we had to take surgery to the wounded. My transport would then be either a truck or else I had to go with the Roman Catholic padre who had a jeep. Once, with the aid of only an orderly, I operated on two men who had multiple abdominal wounds caused by small calibre Japanese weapons. These made correspondingly smaller wounds and so they were more difficult to locate. I had to show the orderly how to pour on ether with a gauze mask, and at the same time had no assistant to explore the abdomen of the soldiers. Our operating table was the kitchen table of an

bandoned girls' school. Alas, one of the men died from peritonitis
ut the other survived.

'About the same time we lost two officer members of our unit.
)ne was the "Registrar", whose job was to keep all the records,
ssue orders, etc. As the replacement did not arrive, I was detailed to
lo his work. To my amazement, I found no difficulty in doing it in
)dd moments between my clinical work. When the new man
rrived, he hailed me as a magnificent fellow to take on such a
)urden with no experience. Alas, I told him that it was such a simple
ask that it needed only an hour to do it on the busiest days. Since it
ook him all day to do it, and that with effort, he immediately
)ecame hostile as he thought my innocent remark was intended to
lenigrate my view of his role. This wasn't what I had ever meant.
Matters went worse when he found I had sorted out the Unit
mprest Account.

'The other change was the quartermaster. The new one was
)oastful of the fact that when he had landed with another unit from
anding craft, one of these had sunk. He had at once reported to the
CO that all his records had been lost in this craft, and he had then
lone as he pleased with the stores!

'His arrival caused more rift between the National Servicemen and
he other officers. We refused to take part in "Boards of Enquiry" if
ve felt they were dishonest. An example was when the QM and the
Colonel tore up fifty brand new sheets and then condemned them as
several times the number which were now unfit for use. We could
1ot complain about what we knew was corruption, and our only
emedy was to refuse to take part in such matters. The Colonel
iccepted our refusal by no longer including us in any future Boards.
I later heard that in Singapore a brothel used by the soldiery was
:ntirely furnished with Army issue blankets. We were not alone; an
RASC officer, who came from a long standing Army family, and was
)roud of their traditions of service, joined us in also refusing to take
)art in corruption.'

Max White is a marvellous man, met already when he was in
Gravesend. 'The Malayan crisis supervened in July 1948' he
emembered. 'I had requested an overseas posting. The 4th Queen's

Own Hussars (later the Queen's Royal Hussars) had just come back from BAOR, where they had been closely involved in the Cold War and had been told they would now be at home for three years. Instead they were immediately ordered to proceed to Singapore on the 8000 ton troopship *Dilwara*, and I was posted as their MO. It was quite a shock. I had 15 days' leave (although I was in the middle of a two-week GP locum in Greenhithe), and got my kit, especially my tin trunk! I went to see the Regiment at Colchester (and perhaps to be vetted!).

'We went out in July 1948, the first unit sent out when the emergency started. We had four subaltern officers to a cabin, but conditions for the troopers on C and D decks astern were not pleasant. I had to give an anaesthetic for an appendix operation on the way.

'The first hint of landfall was as we traversed the Straits of Malacca with the Dutch colonies of Sumatra and Java to starboard . . . my first impression of the Singapore docks area was of the pervading smell - mainly caused by the rotting Durian fruit – a local delicacy. Ignoring the smell, they taste like luscious pineapples, but are very seasonal. The GOC himself, General Sir Neil Ritchie, (Monty's predecessor in the 8th Army in 1942) came to address all of us aboard from a dockside microphone. On disembarking every OR was given a bottle of the famous (or infamous!) Tiger beer.

'We passed to our HQ which was in the tin mining area around Ipoh, by way of the transit camp at Nee Soon on Singapore Island, taking vehicles from a vast car park which had been assembled before the end of the World War for the projected island-hopping conquest of Japan – very fortunately aborted by the atom bombs on Hiroshima and Nagasaki. Rubber plantations extended most of the way from Ipoh to Kuala Lumpur – they appeared to be depressing monotonous places, and it was quite a pleasure to pass some real jungle.

'First we went to the Johore Jungle Training Camp. Because we were an armoured unit, our role was road patrols, not jungle bashing. We would go in for 3-4 days. At first we had open Daimler Mark 1 wheeled armoured cars. The bandits tossed grenades into them, so they had to put wire netting on the top! My role was a watching one. I had my regimental pannier, the large wicker basket

ull of a vast collection of bandages, field dressings, and a metal case
ontaining all the usual pre-antibiotic medicaments. It included the
amous No 9 – the calomel purgative. It was hardly needed here.

'I occasionally went with one or two squadrons on excursions –
on one occasion a 3-inch mortar crew was attached, but the barrel
became vertical in the mud, the mortar shells went straight upwards,
and we all had to throw ourselves flat. The mortar tactic was
abandoned.'

Although Max said his role was 'a watching one', he was clearly as
busy as all the others. He too did a good deal of work to help the
local Colonial Medical Service staff in the fourteen months of his
time in Malaya. As in Africa, they all shared in Christmas family
celebrations 'at 80 degrees in the shade.'

Lieutenant Douglas Cockburn was RMO to the 2nd Battalion Scots
Guards. In the early summer of 1948, the Household Brigade were
all told that because of the 'minor uprisings that were occurring in
different parts of the world, an Independent Guards Brigade was
being formed so that it might go to any trouble spot at short notice.'
The operation was to be called VISOR. 'We were more taken up
with the Trooping of the Colour' he recalled, 'and were surprised
when we were ordered in August to sail, with 3rd Bn Grenadier
Guards and 2nd Bn Coldstream Guards, to Malaya.'

His battalion marched through part of Singapore before moving
to Nee Soon. After 3 weeks' training, they went to their site of
activity, near Kuala Lumpur. The battalion was split up, the rifle
companies being widely scattered, with the immediate logistic
difficulties this created. He had the same range of activity as his
compatriots – casualties, deaths in ambushes, air crashes, infections,
anti-malarial tablets, accidental injuries of all degrees of severity. One
of his rifle companies had a particularly bad outbreak of skin
infestation with Tinea Cruris, which took toll of its operational
strength. 'It made me wonder how they coped in the 14th Army' he
commented. Like all who served with a Guards Regiment, he left
with the happy share of their friendliness and loyalty and discipline,
much of which would not go amiss today.'

*   *   *

Kenneth McKenzie was called up in February 1949, and was very keen to go to Malaya as his cousin, with whom he was very close was in a Guards Regiment there. His cousin telephoned him soon after he arrived in Malaya, and they met at Penang and had several cheerful hours together.

He served first with Gurkhas at their Training Camp by Sunge Patani in the north, and was kept busy medically examining their recruits, and treating their injuries and illnesses while on initial training. After three months, he was moved to another Gurkha battalion, this one about to undertake special duty in an inaccessible area, far from a road, where helicopters were really essential. No helicopters were available.

It was a hard and dangerous task. 'At one time the jungle became so impenetrable that we walked up a river waist high in the water for about three hours which was cool and much easier than slashing a way through dense vegetation. Although I was fit and not overweight, at the end of the patrol I had lost half a stone. The only casualty was the medical orderly who had tripped and fractured his wrist. A perfect splint for his forearm was half a stem of bamboo.

'We ended the patrol after crossing the central spine of hills from west to east, and went down the Kelantan River by boat to Kota Bahru where we were grateful for the hospitality of the Malay Regiment, who gave us food, shelter, and a proper bed. In the morning whilst waiting for the Dakota to fly back to Ipoh, I browsed through an airmail copy of The Times, always about three weeks late in arriving east. As often happens when reading, one's own surname stands out clearly in print – there to my distress was McKenzie, Roderick, Lieutenant Scots Guards, killed in action, Selangor, Trafalgar Day. How thankful I was to have broken regulations and taken the ambulance to Penang for our final meeting. My cousin was leading his patrol and was hit with a burst of fire, severing his femoral artery. His men carried him about two miles to an ambulance, in which he soon died. I wonder if rapid rescue by helicopter could have saved his life.

'A short time later, another patrol ran into an ambush near a village which had been forced to give food to terrorists. Three errorists were killed, our company commander and a rifleman injured, the Captain by a bullet lodged in his jaw and removing a tooth. But he made light of the injury and described the action to me. The Gurkha was sitting against a tree smoking a cigarette. I took off his shirt. There was a small entrance hole on the right side of his chest and an exit hole below the scapula; no ribs had been damaged. There was no arterial bleeding, and each time he exhaled, small puff of smoke came out of each wound. I told him to stop smoking; he looked displeased, and I suspect after my dressing his wound, he would start smoking again as soon as I had gone. Both patients survived.

'I had a radio message to see a man with a leg wound. Given a map reference, we started across paddy fields and scrub lands to meet the casualty. It was midday, hot and humid, coming slowly towards us were three men, escorting a fourth rifleman, staggering and sweating, and carrying a soldier on his back. He put him down for me to examine and to explain that they were walking along a track when the ground opened and the man fell into a hole about two feet deep, onto some sharp strips of bamboo, one of which had penetrated his thigh, tearing the muscle, causing pain and bleeding. The trap had been made by Malay peasants to catch a wild pig for food. The riflemen had carried their comrade in turn for about two miles. They had lashed a seat from webbing straps, probably from used parachutes, and carried him back to back facing aft, using a wide strap around the bearer's forehead to take the load. I said I would take a turn to give them a rest. There was an outcry that it was their duty to carry the man, but I won the argument by saying I was bigger than them, and I was giving an order. Taking the strain on the head and back was reasonably comfortable. After 300 yards, I was happy to hand him back!'

The Guards Brigade completed their 'tour' as the Regular Army calls it. They were followed by another brigade, the 5th, including the Royal West Kents and the Suffolks. Sailing out with them in 1952 on the inevitable *Empire Halladale*, was their RMO, Lieutenant Ian Todd. The new GOC, General Templar, was now in post and was making his presence felt. His predecessor as High Commissioner, Sir Henry Gurney, was assassinated on 7th October

1951, and General Sir Gerald Templar did not arrive until early February the next year,

'I replaced Lieutenant Brown, who had died of septicaemia associated with a tropical ulcer. Medical officers died too, on service. I inherited his 'postman's trousers', the ones with the dull cherry stripe to be worn at mess nights. The Suffolks, 12th of Foot, were an old line regiment who included Minden among their battle honours. They were based on Kajang, a few miles from Kuala Lumpur. My duties were not onerous, so I introduced myself to the Indian doctor who ran the local hospital, hoping to learn something of the people, and their diseases. Despite being short handed, he politely declined my help. I later found that association with the Army would have laid him open to trouble with the terrorists.

'A notorious terrorist, Lew Kon Kim, was surprised by a platoon of Suffolks in his jungle camp and he, with his mistress and a henchman, were shot. Afterwards the naked bodies were displayed in the back of a truck and paraded round the adjacent villages – almost a return to mediaeval customs.

'The troops were from East Anglia, slow, efficient, country lads very reminiscent of the Aberdeenshire people I'd been brought up with. They approached hunting terrorists in the same way that they'd been used to poaching pheasants. They were the most effective troops in Malaya as measured by the numbers of kills.

'They also had the highest venereal disease rate and were not noted for their smart appearance. This troubled the powers that be because efficient troops were supposed to be smart with a very low VD rate! When a platoon came out of the jungle they would stick together, even to the extent of patronizing the same prostitute, Winnie Wong, Titsie Lena, or Mimi, so if she was infected the whole platoon caught it too. I explained to the officers that this was a consequence of the buddy system which they encouraged. They were not impressed. The officers were a pleasant lot and I enjoyed my time with the Suffolks. They were posted to Trieste in January 1953 and I asked that I be sent with them but, as I was a National Service officer, the authorities would not agree. Following their departure I had brief spells with the Cameronians and the 7th Gurkhas – those marvellous men.

'My last posting was to the Somerset Light Infantry, an utterly different regiment from the Suffolks. They were obsessed with smartness, pipe clay and quick marching, and the officers were a far less welcoming group. Their adjutant and I were not on the same wavelength. Soon after joining them I was told that all officers were to be at a mess night the following night. As I had a long standing engagement to play bridge at HQ Malaya that evening, I sent my regrets and played bridge. The adjutant called me to his office the next morning and proceeded to give me a dressing down. He was very rude and dismissed my view that it would have been impolite of me to cancel my bridge and leave three friends in the lurch, so I just told him that we had been brought up with different standards of behaviour and must agree to differ. He believed that NS doctors with a Scottish accent were not fit to be attached to pukka regiments.'

This was one side of the army's work in Malaya – the active operations against the terrorists. It cannot be closed without reference to those wonderful and universally admired men, the Gurkhas. A whole group of National Service RAMC officers extolled their discipline, their bravery, and their loyalty. Captain John Mann from St Mary's, later OBE and a Deputy Lieutenant, with an outstanding career in his civil and Reserve Army appointments in Aberdeen, wrote a memorable account of his two years with them.

Lieutenant C.J.H. Mann was posted to HQ 48 Gurkha Infantry Brigade. 'I arrived at Kuala Lipis, soaked to the skin as the truck was open to the elements. I was glad to have arrived safely and was greeted for the first time since I joined the Army as if I were a member of a family returning home. I was taken care of by Captain Wisset, Royal Hampshire Regiment, and originally 2/Punjab Regiment. This splendid officer looked after a real rookie and helped enormously, even to partnering me to such skill that we won the 48th Brigade doubles championship. He was godfather to my children and a good friend till he died in 1999.'

John was then RMO to 1/10 Princess Mary's Own Gurkha Rifles, at Bentong. His memoir describes in detail their work within the jungle, the ferocity of the engagements, the relief of not only their

own casualties, but also help given to a lorry load of Chines
peasants which struck a rock placed at a corner, with horrific results
the driver and several Chinese were killed instantly. It richly deserve
inclusion as it is a reminder of the great work done by British and
Gurkha troops in helping the civilian community.

'The noise attracted the attention of riflemen of HQ compan
lines and in no time they were on the scene, rendering first-aid, and
rescuing those trapped. The injured were brought in jeeps and
Dodge 15 cwt trucks to the sickbay in part of Bentong Hospital.
attended to them, the local civilian doctor being much under the
influence of alcohol, as usual.

'There were so many casualties with such serious injuries e.g
avulsion of the arm at the shoulder, fracture of the skull, intra
abdominal haemorrhage, that it was obvious that I needed help
urgently. I asked for a Field Surgical Team, and one came from
Kuantan, arriving next day. Meanwhile, the problem was to keep the
injured alive. Control of bleeding, replacement of blood lost, and
relief of pain, were the priorities. Infusions of dextrose saline were
given, but some of the injured were so exsanguinated that blood
transfusion was essential. In a country that at the time I am
describing had no blood transfusion service, and Chinese were
unwilling to part with blood because of a widely held belief that you
did not make up blood you had lost, the only way to give a patient
blood was by donor to patient, the donors being British, Malays,
Gurkhas, and a very few Chinese. All the British and Gurkha
medical orderlies, ambulance drivers, fitters, and many riflemen
gave blood. One British orderly said he was damned if he would
give blood to a —— Chinese. When all this was over, I asked for his
removal as soon as possible.

'The Field Surgical Team did a wonderful job, none of us getting
any sleep for at least 48 hours. All the injured survived, though
several were severely and permanently crippled. After several days,
the FST set off back to Kuantan, and were ambushed by terrorists
who must have been surprised when return fire killed one of them
and drove them off without injury to RAMC personnel.

'At the time any soldier involved in one of these civilian incidents
thought of his actions as part of a programme for the "Hearts and

Minds" of the people of Malaya. They just behaved, and especially the Gurkhas at the scene of the accident, with common sense and practical skill which undoubtedly saved lives. It was enormously to their credit.'

The Royal Air Force was a large element within the British Forces in the Far East. Geoffrey Parbrook, a Birmingham graduate of 1954, went to RAF Negombo in the north of Ceylon (Sri Lanka) after completing his basic training at Warton. He had wished to go to a UK station with an RAF mountain rescue section, or to Germany, as he had a fair skin and took sunburn badly.

'My first evening in Negombo I remember happily sitting in the warm evening air beneath the palms on the verandah of the Officers' Mess consuming a few Pimms in the company of the hospital sisters. I suddenly became aware of a tall figure at the top of which were some epaulettes with lots of stripes. Through my alcoholic haze I remembered something from my early indoctrination at Warton and jumped to attention. "Do you not know you should stand when your station commander comes in?" "Sorry, Sir," was my reply. "And why aren't you wearing proper officers' shoes?" "Please Sir I'm only a National Service doctor and these are the ones issued." Despite this unfortunate start, time in Negombo was quite pleasant.'

His posting to Singapore was to RAF Seletar on Singapore Island. Changi was the main RAF hospital, and there were also RAF Butterworth and Kuala Lumpur. Tengah had a New Zealand and Australian Air Force Station. The general medical problems at Seletar were less exotic than in Ceylon. He did general practice, carried out a survey of 500 patients with otitis externa (Singapore Ear). 'I proudly put my data on the display boards when a very senior Medical Officer visited. I was delighted when he called me to one side, only to be brought down to earth when he asked: "Why aren't you wearing your Malayan Medal?" I hadn't realized I was entitled to wear it!' He enjoyed visits to Kuala Lumpur, and was seconded to the jungle warfare training camp at Fraser's Hill. Kuala Lumpur was one of the RAF stations where there were regular issues of free tins of cigarettes. 'I noted that many National Servicemen arrived as non-smokers and after their two years were fully fledged smokers. Smoking officer colleagues were not pleased when I suggested that these free cans might not be good for long term health.'

The other side was the work within the central military hospitals George Watts was full of praise for the idyllic atmosphere after the hassle of the north and the fighting there. 'We had a very wise and capable CO for whom I felt great respect, as did all the rest. I had another pleasant and friendly group of very competent colleagues.' The only exception was the senior surgeon, a regular officer whom everyone hated. 'The most senior of us had been a consultant before conscription, but he was subjected to the most cruel, sarcastic, and unjustified criticism. His confidential report from the senior regular stated "that this man with a bit of training will make a good surgeon." The incompetent regular decided to examine a highly senior general, and was making such a mess of it, that a more competent National Service surgeon gently offered to complete the cystoscopy. He was shouted out of the operating theatre, and was then told he would be posted to as unpleasant a place as possible for his insubordination. It is noticeable that National Service captains recorded time after time that while regular physicians were often competent and of high quality, their opposite numbers on the surgical side were the reverse.

Lieutenant Michael Drury was at BMH Kinrara, a hutted hospital some miles north west of 'KL' (A junior surgical specialist, he had asked the Commandant at Millbank if he could go to Germany or Trieste. His wife was newly pregnant, and he hoped to go where he could return quickly if any emergency arose. 'I think we can *promise* to fit you into one of these', said the Commandant. Next day his posting was 'Korea.') He too arrived as the bandit campaign was accelerating, and recalled the appearance of West African troops as well as Gurkhas needed to get the revolt under control. He remembered: 'we had about six NS officers, and the CO, physician, surgeon, a pathologist, and perhaps a dermatologist and a psychiatrist. We resisted all attempts to smarten ourselves up, but it was generally a happy and medically efficient bunch of people . . .

Surgical work was mainly trauma – fractures, gunshot wounds, and jungle injuries. A rather high proportion of the gunshot wounds was of face and neck.

'Brigadier Drummond, our ADMS, felt we should understand what troops had to go through on jungle patrol. (This was when John Heber produced his new jungle anaesthetic machine). He arranged for us to go on patrol; I survived, but was flabby and the rest were fit men.

'Drummond rose to higher rank but I had one run in with him. At an "all ranks" smoker, the anaesthetist and I were called to sing something on the stage. We couldn't think what to sing but at the last moment we gave a passable rendition of "We don't want to join the Army." Unfortunately the Brigadier was at the back. He gave us a right dressing down for "incitement to mutiny" and arranged for us to appear before General Templar at King's House the following morning. Dressed in "our best" and suitably chastened we arrived and passed through several offices full of high ranking and tut-tutting officers. When I got to "the presence" I found him trying to lace up some very long boots. "Help me lace up these boots", he said, "this sounds a damned silly complaint. Will you come and see my daughter. She is unwell." I attended her several times but heard no more about "the mutiny." Like all who met Templar I had the highest admiration for everything he was doing.'

This story by the young NS doctor is especially amusing as Captain Drury became Sir Michael Drury, President of the Royal College of General Practitioners. He rose far higher than did Drummond, and in an organization where the field was just a bit bigger, and the contestants immeasurably more able, than the small pool of possibles for DGAMS!

Lieutenant David Weatherall, having survived his voyage to Singapore in spite of his lack of correct wear for dining in the troopship officers' mess, arrived at his destination in early December 1958. After a couple of days of acclimatization, the new arrivals presented themselves at the BMH. Before starting at the central hospital, Lieutenant Weatherall had first to do several locums around the island. The first, at Kampong Tulloch, involved obstetrics, a specialty new to him. He next went to Taiping, where the medical division was run by another National Serviceman, Roman Kocen. At Taiping he was introduced to malaria; where a difficult diagnosis was solved by yet another NS pathologist, Bernard Knight, coming on the ward at 5.00 a.m., having found parasites in the soldier patient's blood. Then he returned to the children's ward in Singapore, and commenced work there.

'The CO at the Queen Alexandra Hospital was Colonel Jock McFarlane, a quiet, pleasant man. The officer in command of the Medical Division was Lt Col J.P. Baird, a very competent physician bur an absolute stickler for military correctness. I think he later became Director General of the Army Medical Services.' The young medical officer would reach the correct diagnosis on more than one occasion where his chief did not. Always humble, Lieutenant Weatherall was quick to praise the experience of Colonel Morison, the Director of Medicine for the Far East Land Forces, and Lieutenant-Colonel Baird, and the help they gave him. But his own level of excellence could not be denied.

'Shortly after I took over the children's ward an event occurred which was to shape my whole career. A young Gurkha child called Jaspir Thapa was admitted with a history of refractory anaemia, the cause of which had baffled the entire medical might of the RAMC. She had been a patient for a year or two in Kluang, was profoundly anaemic and could only be kept alive by regular blood transfusion. About that time I had taken to spending my afternoon off in Singapore General Hospital, where I made ward rounds with the Professor of Medicine, called Ransom, who was an excellent clinician. He introduced me to a delightful clinical biochemist called Frank Vella (later to become Professor of Biochemistry in Saskatoon), who was interested in abnormal haemoglobins in Malaya and Singapore. I told Frank about the patient and together we studied her and her parents and discovered that she had thalassaemia, an inherited form of anaemia which was thought to be restricted to the Mediterranean but which Frank and others had started to see in Southeast Asia. We published an account of this patient; the paper appeared in the British Medical Journal under the title: "Thalassaemia in a Gurkha family." My intense pride in my first publication was short-lived however. I was bidden to the Director-General's office and given a very severe dressing down for publishing this paper. Apparently, publishing material without permission from the War Office was a cardinal sin. And even worse, as the gentleman emphasized, it was bad form to suggest to the world that a top-class Gurkha regiment might be hiding soldiers with bad genes! "Don't do it again" – he told me. Few clinical scientists can have had such an inauspicious start to their research career.'

Another episode concerned his time in BMH Taiping. 'I began to worry because I was seeing far too much malaria. Failure to take malaria prophylactics and catching malaria was an offence punishable by court martial. I couldn't believe that all those soldiers were failing to take their paludrine and I therefore treated one or two cases with paludrine, with absolutely no effect. I wrote to the War Office saying I suspected that we had paludrine resistance in north Malaya. They wrote back and told me I was talking rubbish. I was not surprised however to see in a WHO report written a few years after I had finished my military service to the effect that paludrine resistance was fairly widespread in Southeast Asia!'

These stories recall the wonderful book: *The Psychology of Military Incompetence*, by Professor Norman F. Dixon, of University College, London. It is a devastating exposure by a former Royal Engineer officer of distinguished service of the bullying tactics employed by mediocre and often intellectually challenged military officers to suppress any hint of criticism, no matter how necessary. It is essential reading.

In his memoir, Sir David Weatherall listed some of his NS colleagues, and their names make impressive reading. Fellow National Servicemen were Don Smith, 'already a top-class physician' who later became a consultant cardiologist in Leeds, Stephen Elkington, later gastro-enterologist at the Middlesex, Peter Payen, later a consultant electrophysiologist in London, Harold Fox, later a distinguished gynaecological pathologist, Roman Kochen, consultant at Queen's Square, Bernard Knight, Professor of Forensic Medicine in Cardiff. One of the National Service psychiatrists in Malaya, whose long hair horrified the sergeant majors at Crookham, became later a most distinguished psychiatrist in London. A particular friend he remembered: 'David Evans, a NS pathologist, who later became a renal physician at Cambridge, was a wonderful colleague and we spent hours together looking for malarial parasites.' When he finally left Taiping at the end of his own NS time, the medical wards were taken over by yet another NS officer, Mike Parkin, future Professor of Paediatrics in Newcastle.

Hughie Webb, the top-class sportsman, with Oxford Blues in cricket, golf, squash and racquets, was another who discovered his own life-long interest in viral disease in Malaya. He became the first Professor of Neurovirology at St Thomas' Hospital.

When Hughie arrived, early in 1955, 'The BMH was a large hospital built on the colonial style with large open balconies. There was no air conditioning but the ceiling fans helped to cool the inhabitants from the very hot and humid Singapore air. The hospital was around a football ground, which acted as a landing area for helicopters bringing casualties in from the jungle . . .' He listed the wide range of diseases they saw: polio, dysentery, malaria, Leishmaniasis, filiarasis, tetanus, encephalitis from insect-borne diseases, especially Japanese B encephalitis, leptospirosis, and tuberculosis. 'The clinical experience gained from all of this was invaluable.'

'The RAMC Mess in Singapore was one of the most beautiful sites on the island, on the crest of a hill and overlooking the sea and the islands to the south west. Having drinks in the cool of the evening watching some of the most magnificent sunsets I have ever seen was unforgettable. One Christmas, as we were one of the few married couples, we invited many of the bachelors to our flat.

'Relations with other officers' wives and families, and the protocol involved, rather amused us. On the way out a Brigadier's wife, with children the same ages as ours, had become friendly with my wife, and when we settled down in Singapore, they met up regularly. News of this reached the ears of a senior RAMC wife, and as a result my wife received a visit and a rebuke – as a lowly Captain's wife she should not be socializing with a Brigadier's wife!'

During Captain Weatherall's time, the inevitable Willie Officer arrived, now a General and DDMS. 'He met me in the corridor dressed in my usual white coat with nothing underneath except a pair of shorts. "Are you an officer or a doctor?" he asked me. "A doctor", I (the later Professor of Medicine at Oxford) replied. He was not amused and left instructions that we were to dress for dinner at least two nights a week. We did, but if my memory serves me right it was in sarongs.'

As everywhere else the Forces went, VD clinics, called STC (Special Treatment Clinic), were extremely busy in Singapore and Malaya. Captain John Spence, who was in 'The Last Intake' of National Service at Crookham – and must be mentioned for that fact alone – found the STC at the BMH full of clinical interest. 'At that time (1960) we saw very few new cases of Syphilis in UK; it was quite exciting to find a primary chancre and see the Treponema pallidum (called 'The Stately Spirochete') under dark-ground illumination. We were the first place visited by many naval ratings after landing, people who had dallied unwisely in Bugis Street, and subalterns who traditionally spent their first leave visiting Bangkok and picking up some exotic infection. I remember one unfortunate who had achieved the grand slam, having syphilis, gonorrhoea and Lymphogranuloma inguale.'

'When I arrived at Taiping,' Captain Weatherall said, 'the war in Malaya was formally said to be over, and Malaya proclaimed to be "white." There was still mopping up to be done.' But by the end of the decade, and into the next, things were certainly quieter – one of the few occasions when a major rebel guerrilla force had been so defeated. Malaya was a long hard struggle, and our medical officers, as all others who took part, recalled it well.

CHAPTER IX

Hong Kong

T HE COLONY OF Hong Kong had been taken by the Japanese in the 1939-45 War, and memories of that grim period still remained. Its garrison was both on Victoria, the island, with the mainland, the 'New Territories', across the bay. It had been said that Japanese had swum across this bay when they took the colony in 1941. It still remained a challenge for the best swimmers. The BMH was on Bowen Road, high on the hill and with a beautiful view over the harbour beneath. At this date, Victoria Island was almost empty of buildings, an enormous contrast to the present city packed with skyscrapers. Patrick Weaver, a Guy's graduate of 1950, has preserved with his memoir a striking slide of it. The 'Peak' was even more of a feature, as it was bare and uncovered by building. The Chinese population packed the city, as now, with their fishing boats and their boundless energy. 'The Chinese were far too busy to take notice of us unless they wished to make purchases.' At this time Hong Kong was a busy trading centre with large ships bringing merchandise from the USA, India, Europe and anywhere else where goods were made. The trade with mainland China brought silks in variety and quality unseen by war-time young doctors, and they could buy luxuries to send or take home at ridiculously low prices. On the far side of the island was the harbour called Aberdeen. It was full of fishing junks and larger boats which were used as restaurants. Here, after crossing over in a sampan, the visitors enjoyed meals of fish and other delicacies.

Below the Bowen Road hospital was the naval dockyard. The cruiser HMS *Belfast* was berthed there, with many small gun-boats which travelled up the Yangtse to Nanking. While the staff of Bowen Road had good relations with the crews of the RN ships, they had strangely little contact with the naval hospital itself, which was at the very top of the hill. To reach it, one could take the cable railway. This ran close to Bowen Road, with stops at each level where roads ran round the Peak.

Because of its relatively peaceful state, Hong Kong was a favoured place for short leaves from Korea. But not always. Max White recalled: 'It was possible to pay £8 on an "indulgence passage" on a half-empty troopship to Hong Kong where the garrison had been smartly reinforced when Chairman Mau was threatening to invade Formosa (now Taiwan), whence General Chiang Kai Chek had retreated with the remnants of his National Army. I decided not to risk it as there was no guarantee of a return passage before one's 15 day leave had expired.'

For those posted there, there was the choice of being in the Victoria Island side, and Kowloon and the New Territories. John Donald, whose memoir and reminiscence is the greatest of all, was sent there after being in Korea; he was RMO to the King's Own Royal Regiment, and completed his time with them in Hong Kong. Next RMO was another Glasgow graduate, Archie Hutchison, who arrived in early November, 1954, and following him, in turn, was a Guy's man, Patrick Weaver.

Archie, in due course a skilled urologist at the highest level, who could teach even footering middle-aged general surgeons how to use the resectoscope, was with his unit at the Chinese border in the New Territories. One of his early tasks was to be part of a Demonstration of Atomic Warfare team, run by 18 Field Ambulance RAMC, the Field Ambulance of 27 Infantry Brigade.

'As an Infantry RMO I had to demonstrate my Regimental Aid Post to each passing syndicate, before and after "The Explosion." The RAP was well dug in, as in a static conflict, such as the latter stages in Korea.

'After the explosion, which incidentally quite upset the Red Chinese just across the border, the second site, being well dug in, had very little to show, really quite dull, in fact. For the "after" sites, the Far East Wound Simulation Team had done a terrific – if not terrifying, job of casualty reproduction.

'The other Brigade sites had scenes of awful carnage. The Infantry platoon's position had been decimated with bits of limbs and flesh cast around. The Royal Artillery 25 pounder position was also in chaos, twisted metal, gun limber in tatters, bodies of the gun team strewn around. A 3-ton truck burned furiously, its crew charred, black and cooked. A tank had been blown over. No life – only exploding fragments. Each site was a scene of chaos, with frightful wounds, even to charring, traumatic amputations, arterial bleeding and sucking chest wounds.

'As each syndicate passed by, the hardened regulars, some who had seen real action in Korea, seemed almost unmoved by the Havoc at each demonstration: "Oh aye, quite realistic", while young conscripts were impressed and appalled.

'Finally came the Advanced Dressing Station, the pride and joy of the Field Ambulance. Here was an open-sided marquee set out in a ward design. In the beds were the survivors, splinted, bandaged like mummies, infused and transfused with very dark ink.

'At last, an isolated area labelled "Radiation Sickness". Here were patients, half naked, deathly pale, some with no hair. The smell of "hospital" was heavy in the air. (Ether and carbolic were regularly sprayed!) As the syndicate approached, each hopeless case produced huge volumes of vomitus with ear-splitting effects. Only then were the "hard men" affected, swooning away like 19th century maidens with Chlorosis.

'Real first aid was well applied, with traditional hot sweet tea not the usual fluid for some of the battle scarred troops. But treatment for the red faces was of no avail when they were told that as each syndicate approached, the sick men all took a large mouthful of water with sugar, diced carrot and turnip ready for projection with full sound effects.

'The sight of awful wounds was accepted stoically, but adding sound and smell certainly took its toll of even hardened veterans.'

Patrick Weaver followed Archie Hutchison. He too, would become a urologist in a neighbouring Regional Board area. He found a motor bicycle the ideal method of reaching all the outposts of the battalion. His duties were as usual; his Commanding Officer, Lieutenant Colonel Underwood, asked him to identify himself with the

Regiment, and he found the necessary items made quickly by their Indian Regimental tailor.

'I was an enthusiastic if incompetent cricketer (in fact a very good one) and was delighted to be asked to play for the Battalion, and we reached the final of the Far East Land Forces Cup, played on the beautiful ground of the Hong Kong Cricket Club.

'On a free evening to go to Kowloon or Hong Kong it was necessary to catch the train at Fan Ling, and to get to the station one bought a ride on the back of a bicycle pedalled by a local Chinese; no back seat, seated on the parcel carrier over the back wheel. The "taxi driver" usually asked several times each trip if one would not care for a diversion to meet a young lady.'

When the Regiment left, he was offered the chance to go to No 33 General Hospital in Kowloon. Patrick commented carefully, in his reminiscence, 'from what I had seen the hospital did not offer much clinical experience and the National Service officers there tended to be disaffected with Army life, so I asked to be allowed to stay in the New Territories.' He was sent to 18 Field Ambulance, where life was as boring and unhelpful as usual in such RAMC units.

But there was one diversion there, which Patrick recorded with amusement. 'Life at the Fd Amb was enlivened by the presence of Macaque monkeys in the grounds of the officers' mess. They were tame to us. The wife of a visiting VIP who came one day and admired the monkeys changed her opinion of them when one walked up to her, lifted up her skirt and peered intently upwards.'

He had one assignment of interest. Happily, his later time was with the 2nd 7th Gurkha Rifles as locum RMO. Like all others, he enjoyed it. The obstetrics involved added interest; he admired the ability of the Gurkha midwives. But as he was leaving the RMO locum, he was detailed to accompany a Tank Landing Ship of the Royal Fleet Auxiliary to collect 'redundant ammunition' from the recent Korean War, to be dumped at sea.

'It was apparently necessary for a medical officer to attend these proceedings. Life at sea was curiously formal; I joined the Master and his officers for meals where little conversation was made. (After the trip and safely in port back in Hong Kong the atmosphere changed dramatically; gin flowed freely and a number of ladies were entertained aboard, whereas total abstinence was the rule at sea.

'There were no misadventures with the dangerous ammunition but on the way to Korea I encountered one problem which my training had left me ill prepared for. One of the ship's officers suffered an acute psychiatric illness and retired to his cabin behaving oddly. I went to see him; he let me in and then locked the door. He did not attack me, but proceeded to destroy everything in the cabin. I had no suitable drug, but fortunately the acute phase passed off... While the ship was in Korea I was told to visit three of the few remaining British soldiers still in Korea who were in American Military Hospitals recovering from various minor infections. I was also able to see something of the Korean battlefields, and visit Seoul.'

'When my time was up I was invited to sign on but declined.'

Lieutenant Roy Calne from Guy's Hospital was another who got from Northolt airport to the Far East in a Lancaster bomber, via Rome, Bahrain, Karachi – where with his companions he suffered severely after eating curry in the hotel where they overnighted – and finally Delhi. Posted as a surgeon to the BMH in Singapore in January 1953, he was sent to Hong Kong without warning, then found he was to be with the 2nd Gurkha Regiment, to his great joy.

'This was a vital and enjoyable time for me. Anyone who has worked with the Gurkhas has a deep admiration and love for them. Such continuous cheerfulness and fierce loyalty are rarely encountered. They were passionate, too – first about women, secondly about drinking, thirdly about gambling and fourthly about fighting. Their love of women caused some complications in my surgery: my Indian Nurse confessed to me, "Dr Sahib, so much beauty is a terrible trial and a burden to bear, in this regiment." (She was curvaceous and beautiful but she would still have had a hard time of it even if she had been ugly.)

'My Scottish predecessor in the Regiment told me before he went that all the official medical equipment was in a locked and sealed trunk which I was on no account even to touch, let alone use. All our day-to-day equipment had been the gift from the quartermaster, following the last hurricane. (Hurricanes were like manna from heaven to him because he could write down that everything had been destroyed, including the things he had lost or purloined.)

'I was assigned a batman, who looked after my personal needs: he stood behind me at mealtimes, ran my bath, and looked after my uniform and equipment. Every morning he would bring me a pint mug of tea with curry powder in it – revolting to taste for the first time, but after a few weeks a lack of curry powder made tea taste like water. In the mess, breakfast always consisted of mulligatawny soup, to which we could add, if we wished, further chillies and sherry. The Gurkha officers would invite their British colleagues to drinks in their mess, offering rough and very powerful Indian rum accompanied by hot green chillies instead of biscuits.

'Idyllic as this time was, certain frustrations plagued me. There was, for instance, a young Gurkha recruit who came to sick parade coughing blood and short of breath, with a high temperature. A chest X-ray confirmed that he had tuberculosis, an affliction which the Gurkhas were especially prone to when they came down from the mountains of their homeland to sea level. I prescribed streptomycin for him, but was then told, in a directive from the RAMC in Hong Kong, that streptomycin could only be prescribed for British soldiers. I complained bitterly, and said that my MP might find this an interesting subject to discuss in the House of Commons. The next day, the streptomycin was sent – but my popularity with the upper echelons of the hierarchy plummeted.

'Other directives were equally arbitrary and strange. For example, I had a mule at my disposal for night-time exercises, but I wasn't allowed to ride on it. It carried the forbidden, locked trunk containing the medical equipment. The mule knew exactly where to put its feet, even on a pitch black night with no stars or moon. It never faltered or fell, which was more than could be said for us soldiers, particularly myself, who had not had the benefit of the rigorous military discipline the rest had experienced.

'After a few months settling in with the Gurkhas, I was suddenly issued with a posting to Japan, again out of the blue. I had mixed feelings about going to Japan, not just because of the War, but also because I was so content with the Gurkhas. The night before my departure, my friends at 33rd General Hospital threw a party for me, which was noisy, enjoyable, and somewhat rebellious. After wards I drove back to the new Territories in my ancient Sunbeam Alpine. On the outskirts of the city of Kowloon, I was stopped by a policeman, who wasn't interested in how much I had had to drink, but wondered if I could give him a lift to his village which was next to our camp. I was happy to do so, and the two of us enjoyed the fresh air of the Hong Kong night in my open car.

'The next day I bade farewell to my friends in 2nd Gurkhas and was driven by jeep to a troopship in Hong Kong harbour, bound for Japan. Shortly before the ship was due to sail, there was a loud commotion in the corridor. Two military policemen burst into my stateroom, followed by a colonel who informed me that I was under arrest. The charge was quite clear: I was being arrested for painting a statue of the Virgin Mary outside 33rd General Hospital with gentian violet dye.

'Apparently a fairly extensive paint job had been done, and nobody knew how to remove the offending pigment. I was marched before the Senior Colonel of the RAMC who explained the details of the charge. My simple statement that I knew nothing about the painting and that I wasn't even aware that the statue existed was received with disbelief by the Colonel. However, I suddenly remembered the policeman to whom I had given a lift on the outskirts of Kowloon and the fact that the painting had taken place several hours after my departure. The Colonel permitted the Military Police to make a search for the policeman. He was easily found, since I knew where he lived, and he confirmed the times that I had picked him up and dropped him off, thus establishing my innocence . . . and the true culprit? Much later, a pathology technician informed me – at top decibel from the porthole of a retreating troop ship – that his was the offending hand.'

33 General Hospital had indeed the name for antagonism of National Service doctors to the Regular Army. Whether this was just because those who went there happened to be extra bolshie or not, is hard to tell. But Surgeon Lieutenant 'JP' Williams, with no axe to grind, had no doubt. 'The regular staff treated the National Service

medical officers there disgracefully', he told me. 'There was always a group of regulars, all in their tropical uniforms, then a space where the Short Service officers were. The National Servicemen were put on their own, in their poor, issued uniform and kit.'

Whatever the truth, there is no doubt that the 'FTA Club' was stronger in the 33rd than anywhere else than perhaps in the Canal Zone. As the hospital NS staff left each and every evening, they would all stand outside and shout FUCK THE ARMY at the top of their voices.

Footnote: The extracts from Sir Roy Calne's autobiography are made with the permission of him and his publisher.

CHAPTER X

Korea

THIS WAS THE shooting war of the National Service Era. In June
1950, the North Koreans, long bitter enemies of the South,
invaded South Korea and quickly overran the South Korean Army.
The United States, having troops in Japan, went to their assistance,
initially with little success, and immediately called for United Nations
help. The absence of Mr Molotov, the Soviet Security Council
representative, from the emergency meeting, allowed the others to
agree to UN involvement. Molotov was not there to exercise his veto.

In response to the US call for assistance, Britain offered to send a
token force from the nearest available troops, which were in Hong
Kong. The Middlesex Regiment and the Argyll and Sutherland
Highlanders were chosen to go. David Haldane takes up the story.

'We were given a very short time to pack up and go, certainly not
enough time to bring vaccinations and inoculations up to date. This
had to be done in transit. At the end of August, the Middlesex sailed
to Pusan on the aircraft carrier HMS *Unicorn* and we sailed on the
cruiser HMS *Ceylon*. We disembarked at Pusan to the accompani-
ment of the pipes and drums, paraded on top of one of the gun
turrets. This was the last time they would play together for some
time. Now came our first contact with the Americans and in
particular, the medical services.

'The Battalion, officers and men, were paraded on the dock and
re-vaccinated whether it had been done the day before or not. In
addition everyone was inoculated against Japanese B encephalitis. I
was then visited by the medical personnel present at the port of
disembarkation and issued with the necessities for my forthcoming
sojourn in Korea!! viz six stretchers, a crate of blankets, a large bottle
of Sodium Amytal capsules (for the battle fatigues!), three cartons of
Bismuth Subnitrate powder and three bottles of Paragoric
(camphorated tincture of opium – for "the diarrhoea"!).

Korea.

159

'We now embarked on the tedious train journey to a holding area, before moving in to the line. By good fortune there happened to be an American medical battalion nearby. From them I acquired an RMO's pannier which by our standards was in the luxury class. There was a roll of instruments with which you could have easily done an appendectomy! Needless to say, they came home with me. At this stage we were learning to rough it and improvise, but within a few days we moved into the line in a rather stretched perimeter along the Naktong river. Bn HQ was a farm, so we had a roof over our heads. I quickly learned that any medical help had to be asked for. There was no Field Ambulance at hand for immediate support. In the British Army the unit behind clears the unit in front of sick or casualties, viz FDS will clear the Field Ambulance, the Fd Amb will clear the RAP. The Americans tend to put the responsibility on the forward unit to clear back. We found early on that any one evacuated was liable to end up back in Japan at base hospital!

'During the first two to three week period we experienced some sporadic shelling from a single self propelled (SP) gun on the other side of the river. The companies (rifle companies of the battalion) were engaged on patrols and suffered some casualties. A delay in evacuation occurred because the road route ran along the bank of the river in front of our positions and in view of enemy positions on the other bank. I went forward some six miles on foot to 'C' Coy, to assess the situation. I saw the casualties, and arranged their evacuation by helicopter. The company was receiving mortar fire, which was my first experience of being under fire, and I didn't particularly enjoy it. On reflection I had learned a valuable lesson viz my expertise should remain accessible to the whole battalion by my remaining at the RAP, at Bn HQ, which proved to be ratified within a few short weeks.

'In Hong Kong we were part of 40 Div. But we were now designated 27 Brigade who in theory, were meant to be replaced by 29 Brigade who were being formed by the call up of reservists in the UK. On the 15th of September the Americans put in an amphibious landing at Inchon on the west coast of Korea aimed at driving inland to the Capital, Seoul. This was the stimulus for a break out from the Pusan perimeter and our Battalion crossed the Nakton river on approx. the 20th of September. The river crossing was on foot over a pontoon bridge that was being sporadically shelled by the SP gun and maintained by American Engineers who dived into their fox holes every time the gun fired. I can recall feeling rather foolish marching along with a steel helmet attached to my small pack on my back! Foolish bravado! The Yanks were at least disciplined enough to wear their helmets on their heads. The Middlesex and ourselves assembled on either side of a road heading north and were given the objectives of two hills on either side of the road which were enemy occupied.

'On the morning of September 23rd the assault went in. Bn HQ and my RAP were sited at the foot of the hill (282) beside a small tributary of the Nakton. The assault was successful but the enemy then counter-attacked in numbers and an air strike was called in. Despite recognition panels having been put out, the American planes straffed our forward troops with machine gun fire and Napalm bombs. Needless to say many casualties were incurred (total for the action . . . seventeen killed and seventy plus wounded). The second in command, Major Kenneth Muir, went up the hill to assist in organizing the evacuation of casualties. A number were evacuated through the Middlesex lines but a substantial number came through my RAP. These consisted of burns as well as gunshot wounds. All we had to treat burns, some of which were extensive, was Acriflavine, some Jelonet and dehydrated Plasma (courtesy of the American Medical Battalion). The latter was not easy to administer! I am envious when watching modern TV medical programmes of the ease and frequency with which "lines" are put into seriously ill patients. By the end of the day the wounded were all cleared from the RAP by stretcher or walking wounded until the river was crossed. The hill was evacuated after Kenny Muir had won his VC posthumously and the battalion was reduced to two active rifle companies. By first light the enemy had gone. There followed a period of mopping up. Some wounded Gooks (north Korean soldiers) and civilians had to be dealt with. We received a timely draft of replacements from the UK plus the brigade was joined by the 3rd Royal Australian Regiment. We now had the makings of a Commonwealth Brigade. The Australians brought a section of a field ambulance with them which was a great asset. As a result of being dependent on American lines of evacuation I was unable to follow the outcome of our own wounded except to know that they ended up in Japan. We were now about to embark on the second phase of the campaign.

'The second phase marked the advance into North Korea. It was felt by the powers that be (General McArthur) that the North Koreans should be pursued into their own territory and destroyed, something that was not done in the Gulf war. In retrospect we might have been as well staying where we were, as within a few months, we were back attempting to cross the 38th Parallel again, with this time the enemy being the Chinese.

'The bulk of the battalion flew to Kimpo airport east of Seoul. We met with our transport and came under the command of the 1st American Cavalry Division. The 27th Brigade, comprising ourselves, the Middlesex and the 3rd RAR, proceeded to spearhead the Division in a rapid advance into North Korea accompanied by tanks. Our first real resistance occurred in Sariwan and a freak battle ensued in which the North Koreans suffered heavy losses and we sustained no casualties! The weather was frequently wet and getting colder. By this time we were out of tropical kit and into battledress but not as yet dressed for winter. Because of the continuous movement we were on American C rations which although adequate, meant there was no opportunity for hot meals. There was however a facility for a rum ration!

'The Americans passed through us to enter Pyongyang the Capital more or less unopposed. It was interesting to note that the town was surrounded by first world war type trenches. The brigade resumed the van of the advance after Pyongyang. A number of minor battles were fought involving for the most part the American Airborne, the Aussies and the Middlesex, and I found myself involved with their casualties. The Australian section of Field Ambulance under Ted Manchester was particularly valuable and I was able to assist him when I could. We crossed the Chong chong river and advanced from Pakchon to Chongju just 12 miles short of the Yalu river and the Chinese border. We were to be back in Pakchon very soon fighting a very different battle but we were stood down on 31/10 for what we ainly hoped would be a well earned rest, if not a permanent withdrawal, some hopes! So ended the rapid advance.

'The third phase of the Winter Withdrawal (Bug Out) commenced with the entry of the Chinese into the War.

'The initial withdrawal was in some haste and no little panic due to rumours of a Chinese entry and the fact that we were ordered to withdraw to the Pakchon area without adequate transport. During the next couple of months the Brigade along with the whole army made our way back across the 38th Parallel and across the Han river and to south of Seoul. On occasions we were involved in holding actions, in others covering American withdrawals and on one occasion having to deal with Turkish casualties. At times when withdrawing considerable distances had to be covered, often by forced marches. The first major battle with the Chinese was at Pakchon: casualties incurred were six killed and seventeen wounded. I had evacuated casualties by stretcher jeep, American ambulance, helicopter, and on this occasion utilized a single engined spotter aircraft which landed on a road. Once again I had to be thankful for the Australian section of Field Ambulance. Soon after this the brigade was joined by a superb Airborne Indian Field Ambulance which took all the anxiety out of evacuation of sick and wounded, not that there was much sickness. General health was excellent although there were coughs and colds and skin conditions to which the free ration of brushless shaving cream came in very handy!

'For a time the onset of cold weather posed problems as battledress alone was insufficient to keep out the cold particularly when it became arctic. We were in due course supplemented with American over garments. The dress became, from the skin out: British issue ammunition boots (frequently replaced, on occasion by air drop), woollen socks, string vest, woollen vest and long johns, angora wool shirt, battledress trousers and arctic pullover with neck draw string, American fur lined waistcoat, windproof jacket and over trousers, cap comforter or fur lined hat with ear flaps. This clothing although motley was excellent even when the temperature got to seventeen below zero. Unlike the Americans and Australians we experienced minimal frost bite or snow blindness. I am of the view that the American boot being sealed allowed sweat to freeze in low temperatures. In November and December the weather continued to be very cold with freezing temperatures and snow. Two man tents (pup tents) were still the main form of shelter but wherever possible we would occupy Korean huts or build shacks. The Korean hut had the advantage that they had cooking fires at one end and with a chimney passing under the floor. Rations were still in the main emergency although when static, hot food was available, and essential. As an example of the low temperatures, up to forty below instead of running vehicle engines for ten minutes in the hour throughout the night, they were shut off for ten minutes in the hour. Drinks and shaving water started to freeze if not utilized immediately. Stag duty was changed frequently and small fires were allowed in the bottom of slit trenches. We experienced an outbreak of lice and had to subsequently give typhus inoculations as well as keeping up to date other inoculations. We had occasion to pass through Seoul which was essentially destroyed and certainly not to be compared with TV pictures seen during the Olympics!

'Having reached the end of the withdrawal our last phase of the war was begun viz a slow painstaking advance to once more north of the 38th Parallel. This took us from January to the end of April when we were relieved. The 27th Brigade now comprised apart from ourselves, the Middlesex Regiment, the 3rd RAR, a Bn of Princess Patricia's Canadian Light Infantry, a New Zealand Gunner Regt, and the Indian Field Ambulance. With a Brigade HQ of experienced officers we now formed an efficient fighting unit which along with 29 Brigade (all British reservists) formed the nucleus of an eventual Commonwealth Division.' And in the British part of it, the great majority were National Service men. It was the National Servicemen's War.

David Alexander, son of the Professor of Surgery in St Andrews University, went to Korea as RMO to the 1st Royal Warwicks. As they left on Friday 31st July 1953, on the *Empire Orwell*, they heard that hostilities had ceased 'much to the relief of us all and certainly of our families.' The battalion had the usual run of inoculations and vaccinations *en route*, and arrived at Pusan on Monday 7th September. The train to transport the battalion had two carriages

ondemned by the RMO on account of dirt and faulty axles; US
ailway engineers cut out the condemned coaches and replaced
hem.

'My personal decision' David wrote in his memoir, 'was to get
nyself into the luggage rack which ran longitudinally along the side
)f the carriage above the cold air blowing in through the wire-
1etting windows.' (The train had been used to transport Korean
)risoners of war). 'In due course we passed through Seoul and on to
[okchong, where we were met by the second-in-command and
)ther members of the battalion's advance party and taken to our
amp on the 38th Parallel in Bedford trucks driven by Maori drivers
)f the New Zealand transport unit. Meanwhile, the 1st Bn Durham
Light Infantry, from whom we were taking over, were waiting to get
nto the train and head back to Pusan . . . for the next few days, we
ettled in and got to work. The site of the RAP, although suitable,
vas wanted for expansion of the PRI . . . on the first Sunday
fternoon, I went to Uijongbu to the I Corps Theatre for a meeting
)f the 38th Parallel Medical Society of Korea, which all medical
)fficers in Korea were able to join, provided they could find the
1ecessary dollars for membership. I was lent the appropriate dollars
)y a Canadian Medical Officer and paid my subscription, but when
ny membership certificate arrived with RCAMC on, I sent it back
or correction and never saw it again.

'At this period, so soon after the cease fire, the UN troops were
xpected to be able to man the defence positions without delay, two
1ours being the expected amount of warning, and there were
onstant "Scram" exercises to man the positions. The first of these
ook place a few days after our arrival. Our Battalion positions were
long the south bank of the Imjin and the DLI (Durham Light
nfantry) had started to build permanent defence positions.

'On the word "Scram" from the commanding general, all units
noved into their defence positions. As our camp lay astride Route
.1, our battalion had to fit in between the other units moving along
he road to their positions, especially the Canadian and New
Zealand units whose camps were on the north side of the Imjin. As
ach unit got into position, this was reported to Corps HQ and on
o Army HQ. The Commanding General was hard pressed to

believe the speed at which the Commonwealth Division was in position, until his second in command issued a "Scram" order when he was in the Divisional Area and he saw for himself the speed and efficiency with which the Division moved. This was so fast that the manning of the positions was often quicker than by the US troops who actually lived in their defence positions.'

David was 'stripped to the waist wielding a sledgehammer' when helping his men to dig out their new RAP when the ADMS Colonel Jack McConnell of the Royal Canadian Army Medical Corps appeared, accompanied by a more senior British DDMS. The British officer was annoyed that an RAMC officer should be seen in such a state of undress, much to David's and Colonel McConnell's amusement at his pomposity! 'A mug of hot tea helped to put things right' recalled David.

'Sick parade at this time was three quarters of an hour after reveille and quickly increased in numbers; the reasons for this were diverse, dislike of Korea and army life in general, boredom, minor ailments which were easily dealt with by the company RAMC corporals and above all, a desire not to dig holes in the ground. Obviously there were many genuine cases and in particular skin conditions and sinusitis were common.

'After a couple of months, the CO and I decided an evening sick parade for return cases, coupled with an urgent morning sick parade for new cases would be more effective in reducing malingerers. We put this into action with effective results, but no apparent ill-effects or missed illnesses.

'The 28th Commonwealth Division had three field ambulances in support during the fighting, but the Indian Field Ambulance had been detached to Panmunjon to support the peace talks and there were now only two field ambulances in the Division, the 26th British and the 38th Canadian; the evacuation of sick and injured for us was to the Canadian Field Ambulance who gave us excellent support and who were quickly establishing themselves in more permanent and more comfortable conditions. In support of the field ambulances there was a Canadian FDS (Field Dressing Station), which was in semi-permanent buildings near Tokchon and which was developing into a hospital. Visiting specialists came from Kure –

dermatologist and an ear, nose and throat specialist were particularly helpful. Skin conditions were common.

'Meanwhile, with the approach of winter and frozen ground, digging of positions in the 'Kansas Line' was a major activity, although the RAP was a fairly low priority. Our 'A' company commander, Major Illing, set me a very good example, which I should have thought of, or perhaps should have been advised of by the DADAH (Deputy Assistant Director of Army Health), by organizing the digging of spare deep trench latrine pits before the frost prevented digging. Thanks to him, I was able to insist that the other companies did the same. Not that this was a total success since the 'D' company orderly having dug his pit stole the company rum ration and took it to the bottom of the pit to celebrate, fortunately without serious damage to his health and equally fortunately he was found before sunset and did not freeze to death, which fate befell a member of an Australian unit who did not get into his accommodation one night after a party.

'I went on a three day course on haemorrhagic fever at the 48 MASH in Seoul, where the work was interesting but emphasised a lot of the differences in our common language! Calling the charge nurse "sister" was looked on as a distinct familiarity, and saluting the colonel when I entered his office was obviously a compliment to which he was not accustomed. Off duty life centred round one's ability to use the PX (the US equivalent of the British NAAFI), which, as I was given an allowance of $5 to cover my expenses while here, was rather restricted. On the last evening there was a barbecue to welcome a visiting general (one star, equivalent to a British Brigadier) and once again, I was slightly taken aback by the attitude of one of the junior officers one of whom walked up to the general and said "Say, General, I'm from Little Rock Kansas, where are you from?" I didn't see our DDMS being amused in the same situation! Meanwhile behind the general's back, a bus load of Korean women was arriving for a sergeants' mess party, getting out of the bus at the notice which said: "No Fraternization with the Koreans!"'

David Alexander had a university class-mate, Jimmy Henderson, who was at the MRS in Seoul. They played a joke on earnest US medical officers and nursing sisters who were given the opportunity to 'go to the front line'. Such US visitors always appeared in stee helmets and full marching order, with heavy boots. Jimmy woul telephone David to expect them, and he would arrange for them t be met at the Royal Warwicks' Officers' Mess by a waiter, in whit mess jacket, neat trousers and shoes and carrying a silver tray. H would then greet the nervous visitors with the Jeeves-like question 'What would you wish to drink, Sir?'

John Donald, whose account of his lone voyage to Singapore w have read, was in the same 38-strong intake at Crookham as Davi Alexander and Morrison Dorward. John had a totally differen baptism of Korea – not an RMO and associate member of a prou Regiment, but a single posting and on his own. He arrived at Kure where the BMH was, and as ever, there was no welcoming RAMC staff to guide the arrivals. 'I noted that the small RAMC party wa the only one not to be met at the dockside or provided witl transport. We were just another bunch of green National Servicemer useless and expendable, seemed to be the attitude.

'The atmosphere in the BMH was stifling. Mess life seemed to b minimal and what little there was seemed disagreeable. The furnitur in the anteroom consisted of brown Rexine covered chairs and : threadbare carpet. Drink was frowned on, camaraderie was nor existent and there was certainly no greeting for me. There seemed tc be no leadership or sense of purpose, just a desire to manage the patients in the wards with as little effort as possible. A big night ou was deemed to be an evening in the Officers' Club playing Housey Housey, a game better called Bingo and more suitable for borec housewives than erstwhile officers and gentlemen. I found the atmosphere dreary in the extreme.'

A few days after his arrival, he was ordered to parade before a senior medical officer for a briefing: 'I was marched into an office where an elderly officer head in hand and clearly nursing a monumental hangover, mumbled a few words into his desk top. He told me I was to remain there in the hospital for three months.'

However, John celebrated too well that evening, and was missing next morning from a familiarization visit to the hospital – he had failed to read Part I Orders. The Commanding Officer, Colone

Meneces, saw John in his office that noon. He had already been informed by the Chief Clerk that his name was on a movement order to go at once to Korea. 'He could barely speak for his outrage.' John had been unrousable that morning. 'He pointed to a thick black line on the map and shouted: 'That's where I'm sending you!' I was quite unmoved. I knew that there was no medical unit anywhere on the front line and at the same time I detected his weakness. He had not the guts to give me a proper bollocking.

'We landed at Seoul airport where I caused a little confusion. Everyone had Movement Orders and seemed to know where they were going, transport in the form of jeeps rolled up and my friends of the journey were whisked away. Finally a friendly officer, clearly recognizing the combination of a lost and lonely National Service medical officer and a victim of RAMC administration, suggested he give me a lift to the Transit Camp in the town . . . No one in the Transit camp knew about me . . . the following morning someone suggested I report to the local BMH, which just might be my destination, and someone gave me a lift there. Again I received a less than friendly reception; no-one knew anything about me and they made it pretty plain that they did not care either. No one offered any welcome. What kind of people are these, I thought.'

Eventually, after going in and straight out of the next RAMC unit, the FDS, where once more no-one knew or cared about him, he was delivered by 'two incredibly coarse sergeants who tried to frighten me but did not succeed, to the ADS (Advanced Dressing Station) of 26 Field Ambulance, RAMC.'

John Donald's full description of the conditions within 26 Field Ambulance will come in due course. He was startled to find 'It was an undistinguished collection of marquees and 160 pounder tents. The Officers' Mess was a marquee badly pitched on a patch of bare earth, looking out over neglected paddy fields to low hills about a mile away, and crudely furnished with half a dozen tables (folding flat), several similar chairs, and a crude bar fashioned from empty beer cases. This was the best thing about it. The other MOs were all National Servicemen in a state of mind bordering on mutiny. They ridiculed the CO to his face, refused to talk to him or carry out his orders, which he had long since stopped giving, and even refused to

take drinks from him. The unit was effectively run by the 2I/C
. . . desperately nervous but quite effective in providing a modicum
of leadership. The MTO was an RASC captain, an old ranker who
wandered about stripped to the waist, streaming with sweat and
sinking bottles of local Asahi beer. . . despite his appearance he was
quite effective and was the only officer with any idea of how to run
a field unit and handle men.

'The medical backbone was provided not by Brits but by two
mature Australians – Don Trousdale and Robbie Burns whose family
hailed from Blantyre – they were miles ahead of the Brits in maturity
and plain know-how. (The RAMC were there as technicians and had
no ambition to do other than to see their time out as painlessly as
possible and with an intact skin).They became two of my best
friends. How that unit would have been able to function without
them . . .'

'That evening, quite late on, a large bunch of casualties arrived
and Robbie Burns, on duty that night, was called to Reception. I
was not on duty but it was plain to me that I was not going to get
any decent orders or any training in casualty management so I
followed Captain Burns to the marquee to see what was what and
was badly shaken by the first real casualties I had seen. They had had
their wounds dressed by their RMO at their Bn HQ about a mile
away, and had been brought in on stretchers which were laid out in
rows on the earth floor. Our task was to check their dressings and
ensure that the men were fit for onwards transmission to one of the
US MASHs (Mobile Army Surgical Hospital). The overwhelming
first impression I had was of noise. The men were nearly all from the
Royal 22nd Canadian Regiment, a French Canadian outfit, the Van
Doos (Vingt Doux), who were all screaming and praying for their
mothers, the Virgin Mary and God knows what else. The scene was
unbelievable and I was genuinely shaken. What little light there was
came from Tilley lamps and thereafter I always associate the smell of
paraffin with that awful night . . . we had to kneel down between the
stretchers to better examine the wounded men. I learned to shut my
ears to the screams and concentrated on reading the label attached to
each man, checking them for resuscitation and trying, pretty
unsuccessfully, to say a word of encouragement . . . I saw a young

English officer from the DLI and he had a sucking wound of his chest as a result of a GSW (Gunshot Wound) with a tube drain in place and a valve fashioned from the finger of a rubber glove. This was the most serious wound I could imagine and this was the reason why his voice was so weak and his face so contorted with anxiety as he struggled to get his breath . . . I was filled with admiration for the great treatment these guys get from their Regimental RMOs.'

Very soon, John Donald was posted as RMO to the King's Own Royal Regiment. For them, he had nothing but praise. Lieutenant Colonel W. Scott, DSO, MC, became his hero for his lifetime. 'He steadied me for the first time since I had been enlisted by letting me know that I was welcome to the Battalion and exactly what was expected of me. I was no longer in any doubt about my duties, I knew in broad terms how to carry them out but most clearly I knew that I had been interviewed by a better man than I would ever be, a superbly competent officer and a man of integrity who could be trusted in every circumstance.'

Morison Dorward, an Edinburgh graduate, was yet another who had experience of the RAMC's odd behaviour over postings. He had politely said 'Good Morning' to a senior officer in Millbank who barked: 'we don't speak at breakfast.' Assured that he would get his request to go to Trieste by the major in charge of his intake, he found the next week he was to go to Korea. He wondered if there was any connection! He was disappointed as he had just become engaged.

His job was to run a medical ward of 30 beds in the base hospital John Donald was so suddenly wrenched from. 'The CO, (Col Ambrose Meneces), lined up all the new officers. He asked if any one played full-back, and next, if anyone could teach Scottish Country Dancing. I put up my hand to both. I found I had a cushy posting for a year, playing rugby and running a dancing class in the Officers' Club!'

In his ward he saw hepatitis, diabetes, duodenal ulcers, and 'a phenomenal amount of skin disease, from bad hygiene and from sex with prostitutes, short of getting VD from them.' Morison's later

National Service was in Malaya, where he had an entirely differen
time; we met him there earlier.

Harry Griffiths was a St Mary's man. He was posted to No
Training Regiment RASC in Aldershot, a huge barracks, and wa
telephoned by the ADMS, Colonel P.F. Palmer, in March of 1953, to
be told he was to replace another man who had been taken off th
posting order, to become a Blood Transfusion officer in Korea, a
OC of 11 FTT (Field Transfusion Team). He went in my place; th
reason for my choice as a Blood Transfusion Officer being that I hac
done extra midwifery before being called up.

'Knowing not too much about blood transfusion', he went on
six week course, 'two weeks at Millbank, two at the Bloo
Transfusion Centre in Sutton and two weeks at the David Bruc
laboratories in East Everleigh. The latter involved immediat
enrolment in Major "Toffee" Field's rugby team.'

In Kure, his duties were to the FTT and to the officers' ward. 'Th
hospital had been a Japanese naval hospital and was thus appropriat
to its present task. The FTT was in a couple of rooms at the end o
the first floor of the surgical block. Each of the three upper storey
housed a surgical ward, staffed respectively by Canadian, Australian
and UK doctors and nurses. The ground floor housed the theatre
and sterilizing rooms etc. Our transfusion team was two Nationa
Service lance corporals, one a glazier and the other a diesel enginee
by trade, and later we had attached to us a QA nursing officer. Th
blood for our bank we collected in twice weekly bleeding sessions o
local troops. They volunteered and were rewarded with a bottle o
Melbourne bitter beer, or a cup of tea. We made our ow
crystalloids, having a certain amount of trouble with the filter o
ancient pattern and somewhat primitive sterilization control. W
were happily able to consult the haematologists of the nearby US
Medical Unit at Hiroshima, who were still monitoring the lat
effects of the atomic bomb there.

'Convoys of wounded arrived at the hospital approximately twic
weekly from Korea, having had their primary surgery in US MASH
or sometimes from the Norwegian MASH . . . we all helped with th
secondary sutures and other operations . . . soon after we got ther

he Duke of Wellington's Regiment fought the Battle of the Hook, a roublesome feature in Korea, and this temporarily increased our vork load.'

Harry went to Korea, as did almost all NS medical officers – 'we ill wanted to go. I did in fact three separate periods over there; the irst in November 1953 with 26 Field Ambulance who at that time vere in a certain amount of trouble, their CO having been relieved of his command, euphemistically notified as being invalided home.'

He was attached to the Casualty Collecting Post of the Field Ambulance, and enjoyed bridge with another keen player there. Later still, he was MO in the MI room in Seoul, and finally, was offered the position of company commander of the field ambulance – provided he agreed to stay beyond his release date. Not only did he agree to extend his National Service time, but he did the job of DADAH until finally returning home on the *Empire Orwell*. In his career as an orthopaedic surgeon and in his TA service, where he had a life career of the highest distinction, he always said how useful his NS time had been to him. We learned many years later, when both TA honorary colonels, of our connection as long ago as Spring 1953. We have been firm friends since.

On the RAF hospital side was Claude Sharp, who was transferred from RAF Rinteln to RAF Changi at Easter, 1951. 'I travelled widely as ophthalmic surgeon extensively between Negombo in Ceylon, Cap Nicola Islands, Malaysia, Philippines, and Kure in Japan . . . the friendly co-operation of the air and ground crews was wonderful. I felt sorry for the Korean wounded we were flying back in the Hastings aircraft . . . and for the Australian aircrews coming back from Korea; they were flying Meteor fighters against MIG 15s and they didn't have a chance.'

The Korean 'Medical Base' was at the Commonwealth Hospital in Kure, in Japan. Lieutenant J.A.K. Meldrum, a Dublin graduate of 1951, went there in early 1954. 'I was then starting my registrarship and was only twenty-six years of age', he wrote in his memoir. 'I was given the post of Senior Anaesthetist as I was the only National Serviceman with the DA, (Diploma in Anaesthetics) which at that

time was a consultant qualification. I may as well say a chill went
down my spine. Was I up to it? I would just have to wait and see. I
was a Lieutenant at this stage and serving alongside my Australian
equals who were majors. I became a Captain shortly and my name
appeared in the *London Gazette*.

'The atmosphere in the hospital was very friendly – good
humoured and we made a good team. As a young officer, not having
taken the customs of the Army, I made a great mistake. Drinks with
the Colonel were at 7.00 p.m. and I came into the mess and I said:
"Sir, I am a bit worried about a patient on Ward 3." An Australian
said: "Shop!" – that meant that I had to stand drinks for all the
officers present. It was all in good humour but I learnt my lesson; it
did not happen again. I should have reported it to the Orderly
Medical Officer of the day.

'The hospital was large, I think about 600 beds, when the Korean
War was at its height. When I arrived as part of the peace-keeping
force, the number had dropped to 300. I replaced a Major John
Sugden – when he left I became an acting major.

'It was a splendid hospital, well equipped, and there was plenty of
work to do. I was fortunate in having two assistants, Dr G. Crabbe
and Dr J. Knell. Most of the work was dealing with burns dressings
sent back from Korea. The temperature there was –30°C, and many
soldiers came back to camp having had a bit too much saki, then put
the wrong fuel in their heaters which then burst into flames.

'One of the highlights of my time in Japan was the visit of Lady
Mountbatten. I had the honour of escorting her through the
operating theatres where I worked. She was a gracious lady, but I am
afraid she looked ill; she died later and chose to be buried at sea.'

He had only one trip to Korea, to demonstrate a new anaesthetic
machine, and was back in Britain in 1956, with only a short amount
of his two years to complete. Here again, he had the good fortune
to meet an even more gracious lady.

'Very soon after my arrival at the Cambridge Hospital in
Aldershot I was presented to Her Majesty Queen Elizabeth the
Queen Mother as the officer representing the officers serving in the
Far East, by Lieutenant General Sir Alexander Drummond. She is a
great lady and the conversation was so relaxed; she expressed great

nterest in what was going on in that part of the world. That is the
great gift of the royals.

'The work of the Cambridge was more or less routine. Suez then
broke out. The CO was David Drew, an Australian, later Lieut-
General Sir David Drew. I had not been long at the hospital and I
met Colonel Drew on the way to breakfast and he said: "Good
Morning, Meldrum, you are looking very happy today." I said: "I
am being discharged from the Army in a week's time having finished
my National Service." He said: "I beg your pardon, I am getting a
bit deaf. Have you seen the papers this morning." I said: "No, Sir."
"Read them at breakfast. You are going nowhere – we are at war
with Egypt. Good Morning!"'

The hospital was cleared to receive possible casualties, on the
personal presence and orders of Sir Alexander Drummond. No one
knew what might happen. Captain Meldrum had his National
Service extended. 'Fortunately the Suez crisis did not last long and I
got away.'

His final conclusion was: 'I cannot remember now the period of
my extended National Service, but all I can say is that it went a long
way on my CV when I applied for my consultant job in Birmingham.' Many of us would echo that sentiment.

One of our naval colleagues completes this chapter's account. Wil
Owen, a Welshman who graduated from Liverpool, spent his time
in the Far East, and was actually coming to the end of his service
when the Korean war broke out. He tells of how Royal Navy ships,
including his, were detailed to sail along the coast of the Korean
coast, prepared to 'do a Dunkirk' and evacuate our troops if they had
been beaten by the North Koreans and forced back to the sea. This
story has not been revealed before. 'My period in the Far East did
involve me in the Malayan uprising, the Yangtze incident and the
Korean War. . . reflections produce sadness and a certain amount of
bitterness. The doctor in *Amethyst* was killed. Mrs Thatcher was
rather unwise to suggest that the Falklands war was the first major
military action after the Second World War.'

CHAPTER XI

Special Assignments

URING THE 1939-45 War, on 2nd September 1943, Mr Ernest
Bevin, the Minister of Labour, announced the Government
scheme of conscription to coal mining. 'The Government would not
have resorted to this scheme of compulsion had it not been for the
most urgent national necessity. There is no form of service which at
this stage of the war is in greater need of young active recruits.
Those who are chosen for coal mining will being doing their war
service in a form that is as important as any. . .'

'The selection process was impartial and virtually no exceptions
were allowed. In practice a draw was made from time to time of one
of the numbers from 0 to 9. Men whose National Service
Regulations Numbers ended with the numbers drawn by ballot,
were conscripted to coal mining. Between December 1943 and the
end of the war, some 21,800 men were conscripted to coal mining.
The scheme was hugely unpopular and in the first year of the
scheme, 500 young men were prosecuted for refusing to obey a
direction order, of whom 147 were sent to prison.'

One of the last to be so conscripted, and one who had wished to
join the Army, was John Scott, who later qualified, FRCPEd,
FRCPsych, DPM and an exceptional consultant in his eventual
speciality. 'I swore I would never go and that I was willing to go to
prison if need be. I was also paranoid, in that I believed that as I
came from a mining village and from a mining family, I had been
deliberately chosen. Eventually, on the last possible day, I yielded to
family pressures and agreed to go. My family were more concerned
about my possible imprisonment than I was.

'The regulations defined the training for entrants and this
involved four weeks in a Training Centre in Annfield Plain in
Durham, followed by two weeks training underground. I was an
angry hostile paranoid trainee, and my training made little impact.

The pay was poor – 44 shillings (£2.20p) at the start and 52 shillings (£2.60p) underground. I remember a lecture on how to use a shower to rid oneself of a day's grime.

'I was then directed to a colliery village in Northumberland and the system found lodgings for me with a miner and his wife, in a miner's row which was immediately adjacent to the colliery. Conditions were pretty primitive. The water came from a tap at the back door, the toilet was 20 yards away, and of course there was no running water. The landlord and I worked on the same shift, and there being no pit baths, we had our baths in a tub in front of the fire. First home had first bath. These problems apart, they were a delightful couple and extremely kind to me.

'After a few months I went AWOL, sold a ring for a train ticket, and went home. My reason, or excuse for so doing was this: I was working in a wet section, and for getting so wet, I was paid an extra 6 pence per shift. My workmates told me I was wet enough to be paid a shilling (10p), so I saw the manager, who told me I was getting wet for King and Country, and refused to pay me more . . . I disturbed his office somewhat and left before the police should arrive.

'Eventually, after doing casual farm work, and refusing to return, out of economic necessity, I obtained work in a colliery in my own village. I then began what was my major National Service contribution. This was an old fashioned mine by the standards of the time. I was involved in what was called 'coal getting by manual extraction.' There were no mechanical coal cutting machines, no conveyor belts, or power loaders. There was no artificial light beyond the pit bottom, and no transport to work from the coal face. Put simply, the system of extraction was operated by picks, shovels, gelignite (explosive) and a lot of brutal work and sweat.

'I was a drawer (putter) and my task was to shovel half a ton of coal from the coal face into a hutch (coal tub) which I then ran downhill to a siding to connect it to the haulage system. The most brutal part of the job was pushing an empty hutch back to the coal face. The roadways were only high enough to allow the passage of a hutch and to me seemed like rat holes . . . the hutches often came off the narrow gauge rails and getting it on again, in that very limited space, required a lot of skill and the utmost of physical strength.

'We worked in pairs – a stripper and a drawer. The stripper stripped the coal from the coal face and shovelled it towards me. We were on piece work, so there was competition between six pairs to fill the maximum number of hutches. I had to, and did make sure, my mate and I earned the same, or more, than the others. There were no special privileges or allowances for us.

'Conditions generally were very poor. It was no fun working a whole shift totally soaked by roof water. The air supply was often unsatisfactory and foul. Physical work in those conditions was more difficult. Coal seams were generally low, about three feet high. However, at times some were so low that one had to crawl along the face.

'In a mine, the miner's lamp is of critical importance. I had used the Davy lamp and the electric battery lamp, but in this mine we used the open flame carbide lamps. These lamps were vulnerable in wet conditions, and there were often massive problems when the light went out at a critical period. Without a lamp, the blackness is absolute. In this Stygian state if you turn twice you are totally lost and disorientated.

'Adaptation and adjustment came slowly with the passage of time and my improved physique. I settled to accept that this was my life until my demob. There was some satisfaction in knowing the hardest job in mining and coping.

'It is necessary to recognize that many conscripts were fearful and claustrophobic. The fears of roof falls and of being trapped underground were very real. Injury and death has always been the price paid for coal and most were aware of the statistics of mortality. I think I was fortunate in that having been brought up in a mining village I was in part conditioned to the work, the environment and the fears. My grandfather was killed in a local mine and I had absorbed the culture of the mining ballads like the Blantyre Explosion when several hundred men were killed. Like many front line troops, I always believed that injury or death would happen to the next man, and not to me.

'By 1947 I was still doing my National Service . . . eventually, I had a few lines from the Ministry, releasing me from National Service . . . for us, there was nothing – in particular no medal . . . and not even the right to march in an Armistice Parade . . . in contrast, when the Home Guard was stood down, I received a lovely certificate signed by the King.

'Looking back, I began as an angry young man who came to terms with the demands, became fitter, stronger, and more philosophical about life. At no time did I change my mind that that kind of mining was an abomination and that no human being should be expected to work in those conditions. My service took a big chunk out of my life and I am certain that neither the Government or the people were in the least grateful. We were the forgotten conscripts.

'However, the big question remains – how did my experience affect me as a student, a doctor, and later, as a specialist in psychiatry? Frankly, I was massively advantaged by my experience. I certainly started Medicine older, more mature both physically and mentally. Life in a mining community was a microcosm of the world, one saw it all, the good, the bad and the mad. I had associated with miners whom I regarded as beyond me intellectually, who were miners out of historical and economic necessity. I saw community care and support which is virtually unknown in this modern world. At that time, I supported the Russian communist system, (Stakhanovite) which placed miners at the top of the pay league, with doctors well below. . . During my time in the Industry, I do not think I heard the term stress used. At times, mining could be horrendously stressful, but in the main, it was dealt with by stoical acceptance, by support from mates, by abreactions in pubs and by the family and community generally. It helped to accept the inevitability of stress and was accepted as part of the job. These attitudes seemed to be in marked contrast with the modern situation where even professionals in the emergencies are now claiming for stress related illness.'

My National Service: by Dr J.D. Macgregor

'It all began when, like everyone else of my generation, I was called up for National Service after graduating in 1950 at St Andrews

University, and completing my two six-month stints as House Physician and House Surgeon respectively.

'Unusually, however, I was one of the young medics at the time who were offered a choice between the normal two year period in the Armed Forces or three years (two overseas tours) in the Colonial Medical Service. We were given that this option was a temporary expedient because the Colonial Service was particularly short of medical officers in Sierra Leone and Malaysia. These were the only two territories on offer, though no choice was given to the individual.

'For better or worse, I was one of the group who opted for the Colonial Medical Service, on the grounds, I think, that at least I'd see a bit of the world and not spend a couple of years in a UK barracks looking at recruits all day!

'Arriving in Freetown, I duly reported to the Director of Medical Services, Dr Renner, and found myself posted to the Connaught Hospital there as a general duty MO (just like an RAMC GDMO), working mostly in casualty. This was quite an eye-opener. There were all the known diseases and a good few more.

'After a month or so in Freetown, I was on duty one evening when called to see a man with abdominal pain. I thought he had appendicitis, and rang the surgeon specialist (Bill Quinn), who asked me the simple question; "Is he a native?" Answering in the affirmative, I was rather taken aback to be told that he'd been working in Freetown for twenty years and had never seen appendicitis in a native yet. Furthermore, I was advised in no uncertain terms that if I was convinced of my diagnosis, I should take the patient to theatre myself and deal with the matter. Clearly, Mr Quinn had little faith in my diagnostic abilities. In theatre, I was pleased to have my diagnosis amply confirmed, and removed a seriously inflamed vermiform appendix.

'My self-satisfaction was deflated, however, when next morning I was summoned to the surgeon's office. "You've been here for over a month and you still don't know the difference yet between a Sierra Leonean and a native?", he said to me, and then went on to explain that the locals who inhabited the Colony of Freetown and the adjoining area were descendants of former slaves from North

America, and not infrequently seen with appendicitis, whereas the native peoples from the hinterland of the Colony (the Protectorate) seldom or never suffered in this way. He said that as I'd got away with it this time, he'd put me on the emergency surgical rota.

'This he did, and over the remainder of my first tour of duty I learned a great deal from him of the skills required of the single-handed surgeon in West Africa, where an anaesthetist was seldom available, there was no blood transfusion service, and where the commonest emergencies were strangulated hernias, ruptured ectopic gestations, and Caesarian Section for obstructed labour.'

Next, he worked in a clinic for railway employees, and at first had to use sign language to help. In the afternoons, he travelled out of Freetown a short distance, to visit the Kissy Mental Hospital. 'It served both Sierra Leone and the Gambia, and housed patients of both sexes. It had been built to accommodate some 80 patients, but now had more than double that number, of whom a high proportion were confined by Court Order following some serious crime, e.g. murder.

'A number of these unfortunates were erstwhile students whose schizophrenia had manifested itself under the stresses of university training while in UK or some other northern European establishment. Being highly literate, some of these men produced vast amounts of paper documenting the reasons why they should no longer be detained, or describing their fantasies or fixations with prominent persons, often Royalty, whom they were destined to espouse shortly. Unfortunately, there was little that could be done for them, as medication was so limited then.

'My uniform consisted of the standard white shorts and shirt, and at first I usually wore a tie, but I hastily dispensed with that after being attacked by a manic patient and nearly strangled. As it was, my shirt was ripped to shreds and I had to drive home naked from the waist up. My submission to the DMS for a replacement garment was denied, however, on the grounds that such an event was "one of the exigencies of the service".'

His outpatients clinics were large and exhausting, with huge numbers and major diseases, especially malaria and Yaws. He was later transferred north to Makeni, and promoted to become District

Medical Officer. Surgical emergencies, obstetrical emergencies, and trauma. His was as hard a National service as anyone in one of the Armed Forces, but at the end of his tour he decided to sign on and become a permanent member of the Colonial Medical Service. He served for twenty four years in all, finally as Principal Medical Officer in the Solomon Islands, where he conducted research of high merit, oversaw the elimination of all usual infectious disease (all of which soon recurred as soon as the area became independent), and was awarded the OBE for his distinguished service. 'It could be said, perhaps', he mused, 'that my National Service eventually extended to a total of twenty-four years!'

Dr Allan Dixon was another who did his National Service outwith the Services. During the 1939-45 War, he had with his Guy's Hospital classmates front-line experience of London bombing and later of the V1 and V2 missiles. But when he had his medical examination, he was rejected on account of a small abnormality in one of his vertebrae. 'I was miffed at being rejected, so I answered an advertisement from the War Organization of the British Red Cross and Order of St John (WORCOSJ) for a doctor to join a team bound for Burma "to act as a sort of a local RAMC," and found myself in Hong Kong. From Hong Kong the medical personnel went on to Shangai in the frigate HMS *Amethyst*, famous for its dash down the Yangtse Kiang escaping from under their guns when the Red Army took over.

'There were three in the medical team. Dr Flower, in charge, was an ex-missionary doctor who spoke Mandarin Chinese. There was a doctor from Northern Ireland who had had surgical experience, and there was myself, newly qualified. We were seconded to the Lester Chinese Hospital in Shanghai. The Ulsterman could operate, and as I had been an anatomy demonstrator, I was put in charge of the X-ray department.'

He found the machine dangerous to the staff as well as to patients. He learned to screen for swallowed pieces of gold in newly arranged marriage Chinese girls who attempted 'para-suicide.' He remembered vividly one of his medical orderlies who was a young ex-paratrooper from Arnhem, openly homosexual – 'if he had been a female he would have been labelled as a promiscuous and a flirt.' Another ex-Army sergeant was sent home for too openly stealing from Red Cross parcels and selling the cigarettes and chocolates on the black market. He had a disease he feared was smallpox, which luckily turned out to be chickenpox.

After three months as a 'radiologist' he was sent on to Hankow, nine hundred miles up the Yanksee River. 'We were met there by members of the New Zealand Friends Ambulance Unit, which had been installed in a missionary hospital that was still partly occupied by a Japanese medical team. At the gate a Chinese soldier had a gun and a Japanese soldier had a stick. As long as the Japanese was there we never lost anything to thieves. A soon as the Japanese team left, robberies began. One of the first things to go was our stock of antisyphilitic drugs . . . the diseases were much the same as I had seen in the outpatient department in London, but more severe.' With his Ulster colleague, he was constantly on duty. They had the range of surgery and he had to give anaesthetics by 'rag and bottle'. They watched the young child die from fulminating meningitis.

UNRRA teams appeared: 'their aid went first to the Nationalist officials in Hankow. Distribution of goods was of the trickle down variety. The top officials had control of it all, took what they wanted or could sell and left some to their assistants and their dependants and so on. A small amount, a token, was left for transporting to the communist held area . . . where it was fairly distributed.

'Finally the order came through for us to return to Shanghai. I decided to take my discharge in New Zealand and got a lift on an old Dakota that was returning to Australia after bringing in relief supplies.' He finally returned home as a ship's doctor. For his enormous hard work, Allan Dixon was awarded the OBE.

At the other side of the world, Alan Davidson went to Jamaica, in November 1959. 'I was greeted royally and had been expected "for some time." It was warm and tropical and driven from Palisadoes Airport (now Kingston Airport) to the Officers' Mess to the West Indies Regiment, I was made very welcome and retired tired and happy early to bed.'

His account reads like the sort of National Service everyone would have wished. His Senior Medical Officer, Colonel Welsh, was helpful throughout. The West Indies Regiment was to be formed from recruits of the several places in the then British West Indies, based in Jamaica. The Royal Hampshire Regiment was the other Infantry Regiment there; there were the usual supporting Services, and a MRS, staffed by NS doctors. The CO left all medical and clinical decisions to them. Specialist help was readily provided by various consultants; Alan Davidson, who had wanted to do surgery, found surgical assistance and instruction excellent. In Caribbean Command there were outlying postings – in British Honduras (Belize) and British Guiana (Gyana). The outpost at Nassau had just been withdrawn.

The West Indies Regiment was officered by West Indian officers and the Commanding officer was a Jamaican. Various seconded British officers and senior NCOs were on its strength. From the start, the new RMO established a good rapport; he felt they all wanted the new Regiment to be a success.

All the National Service doctors had the usual run of duties and liked one another. One specialized in care of the large military family population. Alan Davidson's wish to learn surgery was 'whole-heartedly supported by Colonel Welsh, who allowed me study time and access to University College Hospital Kingston anatomy department. I was forever grateful to him for his kindness.'

Weekly visits went to Newcastle, a hill station and 'a place where military families could spend time and relax – it overlooked Kingston and took an hour to reach, climbing quite steeply. I also golfed a little and enjoyed many a mess night with fellow officers, visiting foreign ships or our own warships, as well as the occasional visit to Government House, or Beating Retreat. Life went on very pleasantly during this time and I am the first to admit that my rough edges were rubbed off during this stage, and I made many life-time friendships both within the army and cheery civilians.'

This 'idyllic existence continued to late summer of 1961.' He then was posted to British Guiana as MO to the holding company of the Royal Hampshires, whose medical officer was to return to Jamaica. Initially a little disappointed at leaving, he soon found his new station to his liking. He flew via Puerto Rico to Trinidad, stopping at the Leeward/Windward Islands. After arrival, he enjoyed travel to Grenada, Barbados, St Vincent, St Lucia, Dominica, Antigua, Montserrat, and St Kitts. 'Although we worked hard, one can appreciate that to travel round these islands living in very nice hotels, visiting Government Houses and being lavishly entertained was a dream world and a jaunt which could never be repeated.'

At Georgetown, the consultant surgeon was a former RAMC officer, and here again, Alan had his professional cover, and the chance to assist at operating sessions. The mess was small and friendly. The MRS staff and accommodation were ideal. He used the chance of visiting the local museum to learn about the local flora and fauna. At Georgetown, also, the United States Airforce had a small MHTS (Military Holding Transport Service). They flew to various South American countries, and he had the chance to fly on occasion too.

Being the only medical officer, he had less opportunity of travel. But after doing favours to the US Airforce by treating or flying with their sick from South American countries, he was rewarded by being flown on one of his leaves to Florida, at their expense.

One short spell of local political unrest worried everyone, and some casualties were suffered. After reinforcements were flown out from UK and RN ships appeared, these fortunately settled.

'At this time (1962) rumours were flying around that National Servicemen were to have their conscription extended. I have to say this did not fit in with my plans at all.' That summer, in July, he was told he was to go home. In no time, as it seemed, he was back in cold wet Scotland. He found the medical military there much less easy to get along with! but was of course delighted to meet family and friends again. A short period in Edinburgh Castle allowed him to acclimatize. Then he had the good fortune to watch the Edinburgh Tattoo while acting as medical cover, and to have a short spell in St Kilda in the Western Isles – another idyllic spot, though with very different temperatures from Jamaica.

'My discharge was an extremely civil affair and I was asked by the SMO to write my experiences down for he personally hadn't heard of any RAMC officer, let alone a National Serviceman, with such a wide and varied service. I'm sorry to say I never did.' But he did become a surgeon of note.

Antarctic Adventures.
Dr David Hay was an Oxford and St Thomas's Hospital graduate, who entered the Royal Navy in January of 1958. 'Over many years friends, acquaintances and colleagues have told me of their National Service with varying degrees of enthusiasm; many have been bored and resentful. For me it was amongst the happiest times of my life.'

After an introduction to naval life on HMS *Chicester* during its sea trials, where he learned 'about the workings of a small ship', and a course at RNH Haslar, he joined the Antarctic guardship HMS *Protector* on 22nd July. His account from then onwards is a fascinating one.

'The ship had been built in 1936 by Yarrow's in Glasgow as a fast net layer, a ship of 3,500 tons with an honourable record of service in the Second World War in Norway, the Mediterranean, and the Far East. In 1954 it had been converted into an ice patrol ship with a flight deck aft and a rather unsightly hangar which housed two Westland Whirlwind helicopters. Its role was to support the Falklands Islands and their dependencies such as South Georgia, also to deliver mail and supplies to the British Antarctic bases. The ship carried 30 Royal Marines for training in cold weather warfare and survival techniques. Later I had to extricate one marine with a broken elbow from a crevasse. Incidentally, and very much as a subsidiary, it did a little surveying and collected meteorological data.

'We sailed in the equinoctial gales via Bermuda to the Panama Canal and on to Callao, the port for Lima in Peru. There much of the ship's company went up the Andes by the central railway to Rio Blanco. We then travelled down the west coast of South America to visit Valparaiso in Chile and several of us went up to Santiago for two nights. Our passage then took us through the Magellan Straits via Punto Arenas to the Falkland Islands, our base for the next five months.

'Here we visited South Georgia and Deception Island several times and all of the Antarctic Bases on the Graham Land Peninsular and its associated islands at least once. In order to give the matelots a run ashore we had a week-long visit to Montevideo in February.

'A highlight of that summer season in the Falklands was when Dr Stewart Slessor, the Government medical officer at Port Stanley, asked me to relieve him whilst he took some sick leave for a few days. I was flown in a small Beaver sea-plane to each call. The farms are mostly close to the creeks, inlets and coves around the coast of the Islands, which are together the same size as Wales. The pilot skilfully landed the plane near the farm and I was taken ashore with my bag by a rowing boat and thence by horse to the patient. On one such occasion, at Charters, the fog was so dense that both the pilot and I spent the night as guests of the Luxtons. That was an antenatal visit and I recently communicated with the child concerned, who is now 42 years old!

'Our return from from the Falklands was via Tristran da Cunha. There I was flown ashore by the ship's helicopter to attend the local doctor who was suffering from alcoholism, and whom we evacuated to South Africa, leaving the medical care of the 250 inhabitants in the capable hands of Sister Brent, a Nightingale trained at St Thomas's.

'Ten days in South Africa were followed by visits to Ghana, Sierra Leone, and Gibraltar. It was a long trip, some 50,000 miles with an unusually large amount of sea-time. We were at sea on Christmas Day, which is extremely rare in peace-time. There were twenty officers in the Ward Room and they made me extremely welcome. We keep in touch and two or three have become friends for life. I developed an affection for "Jolly Jack", who has all the fine qualities which until recently we were allowed to think of as typically British – resourceful, stoical, and at his best in adversity. For the Petty Officers I developed huge respect.' His was a special assignment indeed.

Research – clinical and atomic
National Service medicals were not asked to undertake any research as such, although it might have been sensible if their Regular superiors had had the good sense to realize how men with the intelligence so many conscripts brought with them could have done

so. There were a few exceptions to this generalization, and one of these was Flying Officer George Forwell.

Problems associated with flying and those who flew were investigated at the Institute of Aviation Medicine in the Royal Aircraft Establishment, Farnborough, Hampshire. It lay beside the Portsmouth Road, A325, (now A331) south of Camberley and north of the Aldershot military garrison area, but had an atmosphere very different from either of these.

From the last stages of the 1939-45 war there was the problem of pilots 'blacking out' during tight turns. At first water suits were tried to increase pressure on their lower limbs, and this prevented loss of consciousness. The next stage was to wear a suit using air pressure instead of water. Initially, there were no centrifuges, so the doctors had to test suits in aircraft.

Next, work began on the 'ejector seat' and the first researchers had the experience of having their heads forced forwards onto their chest.

George Forwell graduated from Edinburgh in 1950. He was house physician to Sir Stanley Davidson. Most unusually at that date, he was given a research grant to study blood coagulation as a PhD project. Called up in May 1952, he was posted as a GDMO to RAF Boscombe Down. When he went home on leave, he met Sir James Learmonth, Regius Professor of Surgery in Edinburgh, and his former surgical Chief. Learmonth told him: 'You don't want to be a station MO – you should go to the Institute of Aviation Medicine.' Sir James was then Consultant to the Royal Air Force, so when he wrote to the RAF Medical Director General, the MDG naturally complied, and young Forwell was transferred.

'I was the only National Serviceman there', George told me as he recounted his memories. 'I lived in the No 1 RAF Mess – dinner nights were quite something. The Group Captain was Bill Stewart of Glasgow and Roxburghe the Wing Commander. They felt I'd been imposed on them. So I had to justify myself. Also we were dogged by Americans, who wanted to know what we were up to – there were several problems on the go at that time. The Top Brass loved to bring people from San Antonio. We had a lot of visitors – they were all spies.

'Man was going through the sound barrier – hence had to be equipped with a g-suit and an air ventilated suit.

'A climate lab was built in 1950. I worked there. Especially in hot climates, where pilots sat for ten minutes on the ground before take-off, some blacked when they took off and fell into the sea. About six or seven pilots were lost, especially from aircraft carriers. We found the reason was that they got *too hot* and a means had to be found of keeping them in thermal balance. A suit with 120 jets of air, plugged into the aircraft, was devised. The tube was disconnected when the plane took off. (see "Flying personnel Suit: Air Supply Requirements" in *Flying Personnel Research Committee* report of June 1953)

'My own contribution, because I had some experience in haematology, was to work out whether the blackout was related to the white blood corpuscles – but my work wasn't very interesting.

'What was the main thing was the question of sweat. I worked with a National Service AC2, Michael Bulmer, who was a statistician, and a very good one. He resented his rank. His father was Dr Ernest Bulmer, Chief physician in Birmingham. We had money and the lab to produce the conditions. I've never worked so hard in my life . . . there were many false trails . . . we did crazy experiments, such as putting pads on the feet of pilots going to 10,000 feet – to measure the Sodium and Potassium in the sweat. But our work has stood the test of time.' (see 'Sodium and Potassium in Thermal Sweat' by M.G. Bulmer and G.D. Forwell, November, 1954, and the *Journal of Physiology*, 1956, 132, No 1, p115 'the Concentration of Sodium in Thermal Sweat' by same authors.)

He also helped with work on ejector seats. 'If you ejected too high, you became anoxic – so how to get the chap down. In the first Martin Baker ejector seats, when you baled out the pilots were incapable of *doing* anything, so you had to make a device which, as the pilot got nearer the ground, put out the main 'chute. We produced a "femoral length" (a length of the man's femur bone) – if it was too long, he hit his head, etc. The "femoral length" was not directly proportional to the total height.'

They also worked on the effect of decompression. 'In Spring of 1954, two Comets were lost. We had a rush of Americans, desperate to catch up on Britain.' He remembered 'the return of the corpses, the diagnosis of death by explosive decompression, the testing of Comets to destruction in the tank, the discovery that the windows were too big, the need to make them smaller, by which time the US had introduced these in the Boeing, and Britain lost out.'

The behaviour of the seniors towards his colleague Bulmer angered him. 'They were not interested in AC2 Bulmer. I made representations to the CO about promotion for him. We used to meet for coffee each morning to discuss "the problem of the day" – but this was only for officers. Stewart was not receptive to my efforts to have Bulmer up-ranked.

'At No 1 RAF Mess, procedure was absolutely rigid, by rank. I was deputy drinks officer, as I didn't drink. Flying Continuation Training was mixed with dining in nights. We sat down to discuss the menus. If the DG was to be present, "we had to have everything at the dinner." If we wanted Kiwi fruit, a Canberra was sent to New Zealand, South Africa, all over the place, to get fruit, wine, for this dining in night. "Flying Continuation Training" was how the Canberras flew, to collect these rarities!'

A National Serviceman at Christmas Island, 1958

Kingsley Robertson was at Trent College when National Service was introduced. After graduating from Westminster Medical School, and as he wanted to do surgery, and wanted to make the best use of his two years, he would try and obtain an 'extra' qualification. 'With a career in surgery in mind, I found that one could get a further three months deferment to study for the Primary Examination of the Royal College of Surgeons. The examiners were kind and I passed . . . within days of receiving the result I had notification to attend for a selection interview at No 100 Richmond Terrace, Whitehall. A group of five recently qualified doctors were interviewed to find out why we wanted to be in the Royal Air Force and why we were not applying for a Short Service Commission. They seemed to appreciate my reasons not to apply for the three years service and recorded my interest in surgery.'

He entered the RAF in June, 1956. His aim to do surgical training was fulfilled. However, 'the AVM (Air Vice Marshal)

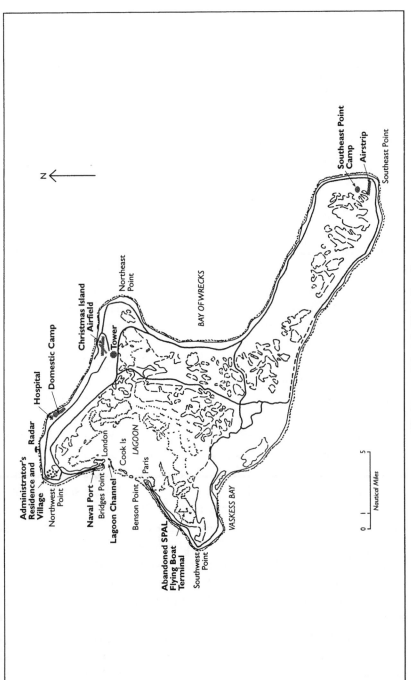

Christmas Island (Kiritimati).

191

summoned me to the operating theatre at the beginning of December 1957, to ask me if I would be prepared to go to Christmas Island for the last of my time in the RAF, as my colleague who had been posted there had been medically downgraded. I accepted with the provision that I had a baggage allowance that would allow me to take surgical books for reference and study. This was agreed.'

The net day he received orders to return to Warton for a further course on Radiation Medicine and Physics. It was well arranged, as the Services do at their best, and after a few days' leave, Flight Lieutenant Robinson received his movement order to report at RAF Lyneham on the 11th of December, for a night in transit quarters before a morning departure for Christmas Island the following morning. The aircraft was to be a De Havilland Comet C2 recently introduced, since the modifications arising from the tank studies at Farnborough which had been carried out and the structural faults which led to the loss of the early Comet airliners had been corrected.

The first leg was to Keflavik in Iceland, where they had breakfast, courtesy of the American Air Force. 'In less than two hours we airborne again' by way of Goose Bay in Labrador for another breakfast, and next landing was at Offutt Air Force Base, Nebraska, the home of the American Air Force Strategic Air Command. 'Very secret at that stage of the Cold War, we did not get a glimpse of a B-47 or a B-52, but we did get another breakfast, surrounded by US personnel. It was nearly midnight.'

Next leg was over the Pacific Ocean. At Hickham Field and Air Force Base, with Pearl Harbor adjacent, their Comet seemed tiny beside all the Douglas Globemasters, DCs 3, 4, 6 and 7, and Lockheed Constellations. 'Although representing more advanced technology, the Comet seemed extremely small beside all these monsters. The RAF had a presence at Hickham Field, a rented hut, two Landrovers and a Standard Vanguard Van – to facilitate movement of aircraft, stores, equipment and personnel for the operation on Christmas Island.

'Christmas Island (Kiritimati) is the world's largest coral island, being "Y" shaped and forty miles long, the central lagoon was almost enclosed, but with a narrow channel through the reef to the open sea, the area chosen for the port and the naval presence. On the north side of the island was a Gilbertese village with a population of 300 Gilbertese who were organized transients, Melanesian workers and their families recruited from the other islands to harvest the copra crop from the planted palms on the island. As it was a British Protectorate, there was an Administrative Officer and his wife who lived beside the village which was entirely self-sufficient.

'The remoteness of the island, the long extension to the south east point, and availability of good runways with a good port facility, all led to its selection for the continuation of the nuclear test programme commenced in Australia on 3rd October, 1952. The OPERATION GRAPPLE programme commenced in May 1957, May 15th, May 31st, and June 19th, with airbursts close to the unpopulated island of Malden. These were followed by GRAPPLE X, an airburst 2.5 Km from the south east point of Christmas Island, on November 8th, 1957, and the next projected test was thought to be in April or May 1958.'

His fascinating and detailed account includes terrain, climate, the feeling of universal depression during the Christmas after he arrived, the monotony and the rainfall, the staffing, the medical facilities – 'some yards away from the dental surgery was a nondescript hut with overhanging roof. This was the pathology laboratory, run by a technician corporal, and the operating theatre. My heart sank at the sight of this, a portable fixed height painted iron operating table of 1914 design, stood under a 100 watt lamp with a home made reflector. There was an adequate Boyle anaesthetic machine, with laryngoscopes, masks, and endotracheal tubes. The suction was a foot operated pump. There were instruments for basic surgical procedures and one could do an appendicectomy. However I lost no time in signalling (telegram message) to the task force headquarters requesting an adequate surgical light and a modern operating table. Within two weeks they were flown to us. The ward was a large marquee with fifteen beds, its own latrines and washing facilities.

'We wore shirts, open neck and shorts, khaki tropical issue with socks and black shoes. Only the RAF blue beret and the shoulder stripes with brass medical collar dogs indicated that we were RAF medical officers and very soon the sun faded the beret to a pale grey, while the gold braid of the cap slowly turned green! It was only after wearing shorts for several weeks and observing those around me, that I realized that hair should grow over the patella (knee cap); it is only the friction from long trousers that removes it at home . . . the conditions for all were similar; every one lived under canvas, only the number allocated to each tent varied . . . the Commanding Officer, the 'Boffins' (scientists from AWRE – Atomic Warfare Research Establishment) had single accommodation in the same sort of tents . . . the food was similar in all messes.

'On the island, every few days brought more personnel of all three Services. Nearing the time of the test a Senior Medical Officer was posted to the hospital, a Wing Commander on detachment for the duration of the test programme – we felt somewhat put out by this, but it did give us the opportunity to fly and leave the island for short periods . . .

'The arrival of senior members of AWRE, and high ranking officers, signalled the approach of the test. They were accommodated in the Task Force commander's Mess tent adjacent to the officers, and only expected to be on the island for a few days, if the weather allowed the drop on the day planned.

'Preparations included a very accurate roll-call and checking procedure to ensure everyone on the island was accounted for at the time of the test. Each unit was responsible for this, the hospital included. We were already in a state of readiness in view of the intensive flying programme which preceded the test. The sea was under surveillance by the Shackleton aircraft, the radar installations were accurately calibrated for all distances and heights by the Canberras, who also made the meteorological readings necessary to confirm the conditions for the weapon test.

'The weapon was to be dropped 2.5km from the South-East point to detonate at a height of 2350 metres. The weapon was a free falling bomb of 1 megaton explosive power. As such it would be a clean explosion as no solids or water vapour would be drawn up from the surface that could later cause fall-out. There would be the usual initial light flash followed by the sound wave, followed by the blast wave. At the range predicted there would not be any radiation reaching anyone involved in the test: provided the aircraft were able to follow the planned flight paths, they would be monitored and washed down at the decontamination area after touchdown. One of the Canberras equipped for the highest air sampling was fitted with a scorpion rocket motor; this caused some anxiety as the peroxide fuel needed special storage and posed considerable hazard to the ground crews. The personnel on the island and the Gilbertese were not exposed to risk if simple precautions were observed. The flash could cause retinal damage, but there was no danger of this if the eyes were shut and covered at the time of the flash. Skin damage was unlikely but everyone was to be issued with a white overall with gloves and a naval anti-gas hood as used in naval gun turrets. All the buildings on the island, being huts, were vented by partial dismantling to allow the blast wave to pass through.

'While the aircraft and scientists had a rehearsal for the drop, we checked all the procedures in the hospital, and briefed our personnel. A public address system had been set up to communicate with every person on the island, either at their stations or marshalled outside in groups, to avoid blast injuries. The hospital crew paraded in the open area beside the hospital at 09.00 hours. The roll-call was correct, including our three in-patients who were fortunately well enough to stand out in the open at the time of the drop. All attired in the protective white garments, we were addressed by loudspeaker, being given instructions about the procedure, an outline of the commentary, and the object of the test. Finally a message from the Task Force Commander, and the commentator took over. Music was provided to pass the time and improve morale. We felt his choice of Elvis Presley singing "I'm all shook up" was not in the best taste, but a light hearted atmosphere prevailed. It was a perfect day, warm, light wind and a few fluffy clouds.

'The music was interrupted by the commentary: "The Valiant with the weapon is now lined up for take-off, the Valiant is now airborne and will reach its operational target in fifteen minutes." More music, then: "The Valiant is now commencing its first target run. This will be a dummy run." Nevertheless we were instructed to sit facing away from the ground zero at the south east point with eyes covered, until given the instruction to uncover eyes and stand up.

'More music, then: "The Valiant is now commencing the first live run", a pause, then the order to sit down and cover the eyes, before a count-down to ten. "The weapon is dropped." A slight warmness felt at the back of the neck was the only indication that the explosion had occurred, until the loud bang, and then, just as you thought nothing else would happen, a thumping gust of wind, neither damaging enough to either ears or body. "You may now open your eyes and look at the cloud." Ten seconds from the explosion the fireball was already covered with a condensation white cloud through which the yellow-orange glow was clearly seen, the whole rising into the sky, leaving the stalk of the mushroom cloud in evolution. As the fireball rose upwards, the colour became more pink-red and obscured by a rapid darkening of the enveloping cloud, increasingly diluted by further white cloud to form the mushroom as the fireball colour faded. Eventually, at a great height, the cloud began to get distorted as the altitude winds caused it to drift very slowly and disperse. It was more than half an hour before the last traces of the cloud were gone.

'Once it was certain that the cloud posed no threat to the island, we were dismissed, and returned to normal duties. There was a delay before we were dismissed, as a variation in the high altitude wind caused some anxiety that the cloud might drift back over the island. In the event, it did not.

'The first priority was to restore the buildings and tents to their proper condition. As a result of the venting procedures, there was no structural damage at all. Panels were replaced, tent walls lowered, doors closed, and everything quickly returned to normal. The flying programme continued to be very active, monitoring the atmospheric effects and taking air samples. The Valiants involved in the drop soon returned, having executed the racetrack pattern to line up for the live drop. All except the bomb aimers' windows were covered by interior shutters; as soon as the weapon was released, they had to execute a steep left turn to get them out of danger, and then, when the shutters were released, the crew could observe the cloud.

'The sampling sorties continued for several days. On the return of the Canberras, they taxied to the decontamination area for Geiger counter screening, then a hose down, while the aircrew were also monitored, changed clothing, and showered, before final monitoring and release. I took the opportunity to visit the area to see the procedures for myself. At the conclusion, I was monitored, and caused great alarm by having the highest reading they had encountered! This proved to be due to the thorium used in the luminous numerals on my quite expensive Swiss Omega wrist watch. While not a serious problem, it served to show how little hazard there was involved in the weapon test. (Thorium is no longer used in luminous paints for clocks and watches.)

'After the test, there was a sense of anticlimax which persisted. All those who had been on the island for some months turned their thoughts to home. For the medical officers, this depended upon when one's replacement could be expected. For the others the Flying Constellations were taking all the temporary posted servicemen off the island every day. The Valiants left for their home base in Wittering, the Shackletons departed, and as the sampling sorties concluded, they too left for UK. The next test, GRAPPLE Z, was scheduled for August, the next build up would be in June and July.

'During this period the Royal Engineers were able to upgrade the hospital; they now had a surplus of time and materials. We sat down with them and designed a new ward and a replacement operating theatre. Both were to be timber framed on a concrete base, clad in corrugated aluminium sheet, with louvered glass windows and free ventilation at floor level and below the roof. The ward was completed very quickly and had fifteen beds, with toilet and washing facilities at one end and treatment room at the other. The operating theatre was more complex, to be dust proof it had to be air conditioned. The light and table were transferred from the old hut, and we had a new autoclave which was difficult to install. There was an anaesthetic room. It was not as spacious as we had hoped, but they had to use the available materials. By the time it was finished, my replacement arrived.

'I decided I would try to return westwards from the Far East, to make a world circuit. The Hastings Mk1 went to UK via Australia and Singapore. On 17th May my replacement arrived on the Comet flight and was subjected to the fastest ever hand-over so that I could catch the Mk1 Hastings, leaving the next day, the 18th May.'

He returned by way of Fiji, Brisbane, Darwin, Singapore, Kuala Lumpur, Ceylon, (where there was bad civil unrest) Goa, Bahrain, Malta, and at last to RAF Lyneham. He found it 'well equipped to handle the discharge of servicemen from overseas, and the formalities of medical examination, completion of discharge documentation, surrender of RAF form 1269, the identity and pass card, and I was free to leave. The kit issue was not returned as the National Serviceman was retained on the Reserve for a further six years, which fortunately did not involve any duties at all. I was met at the gate of RAF Lyneham by my mother and step father and taken back to normal life as a civilian once again and the English summer climate.'

The end of this narrative is fitting as the epilogue to our tale. We, the National Service doctors, did indeed circle the world – a wider British world than today's newly qualified can ever imagine. We maintained the health and treated the injury of those our country sent to serve in all those places.

The National Servicemen held the fort for 15 important years in the 20th century. They swelled the ranks of our Armed Forces at a time when our nation, because of its tiny population, could not otherwise have produced the numbers needed to garrison the West, deter the East, and support emergent countries world-wide. They did everything asked of them and so merit your acknowledgement; they were in no way only a collection of the disaffected and unhelpful. The full-time element in the three Services for the most part used them well, and the part-timers were – as this story shows – sympathetically critical when they were used less happily. But unlike the Regulars, they were not afraid to comment if they saw dishonesty, vindictiveness, or incompetence. Nothing like the National Service Era has ever happened before, and we can be reasonably sure nothing like it will ever happen again.

National Service Medical Officers' Archive

1. Agnew, Dr R.A.L., General practitioner, Ormskirk
2. Alexander, Dr David, Consultant radiologist, Warwick
3. Arnold, Dr E.R., General practitioner, Kent
4. Armstrong, Dr Andrew, General practitioner, Lockerbie
5. Ashworth, Dr Brian, Consultant neurologist, R.I.E.
6. Ashken, Mr Michael, Consultant surgeon, Norwich
7. Aust, Professor J. Bradley, Dept of Surgery, S. Antonio, Texas
8. Bailey, Mr Bruce N., Consultant plastic surgeon, Aylesbury
9. Bamforth, Dr John, Consultant physician, Southampton
10. Beavon, Dr Paul, General practitioner, Hurley, Warwickshire
11. Bevan, Professor Peter G., CBE, Surgery, Birmingham
12. Beveridge, Dr George, Consultant dermatologist, Edinburgh
13. Begg, Dr Tom, TD, Consultant physician, Glasgow
14. Bell, Mr Sandy, late A & SH, patient, Forfar, Angus
15. Bennett, Dr John W., General practitioner, Gloucester
16. Billinghurst, Dr John, Consultant physician, Africa and Essex
17. Blair, Mr John S.G., OBE, TD, Consultant surgeon, R.I. Perth
18. Blueglass, Prof Robert, CBE, Professor of psychiatry, Birmingham
19. Boyd, Dr David, Consultant physician, Edinburgh
20. Boyd, Dr J.F., Chest physician, Glasgow
21. Bradford, Dr Norman, General practitioner, Southampton
22. Braid, Dr Donald, Consultant anaesthetist, Glasgow
23. Brain, Dr Michael, Canada
24. Breed, Dr J.H., Consultant anaesthetist, S. Manchester
25. Brudenell, Mr Michael, Consultant obstetrician, Kent
26. Bruggen, Dr Peter, Consultant psychiatrist, London
27. Buckley Dr Barry, Consultant anaesthetist, Carlisle
28. Burgess, Dr John N., General surgeon, Syracuse, New York
29. Burwell Professor R.G., Ortho and spinal disorders, Nottingham

30. Cairns, Dr Charles, Consultant anaesthetist, Glasgow
31. Caldrey. Dr John, General practitioner, Devon
32. Calne, Sir Roy, Cambridge
33. Campbell, Professor A.G.M., Child Health, Aberdeen
34. Carreras, Dr Joe, General practitioner, London
35. Cavanagh, Dr A.J.M., General practitioner, Brecon
36. Chamberlain, Prof Geoffrey, Swansea
37. Christian, Dr R.P., Police Surgeon and G.P., Isle of Man
38. Clark, Dr Fred, Consultant physician, Newcastle
39. Clarke, Mr Peter, OBE, Aberdeen, Consultant dental surgeon
40. Cockburn, Dr Douglas, General practitioner, Elie, Fife
41. Cohen, Dr Cyril, OBE, JP, Consultant geriatrician, Angus
42. Coles, Dr Ross, Consultant ENT surgeon, Nottingham
43. Conway, Mr J.S., Consultant ophthalmologist, London
44. Coni, Dr Nicholas, Consultant geriatric physician, Cambridge
45. Cook, Major-General Arthur T., Physician, Hants. (Regular)
46. Cook, Dr Gordon, Physician and medical historian, London
47. Coull, Mrs Mildred (wife), Fleet, Hants
48. Craig, Dr D.G., Company Medical Adviser, ECII, Europe
49. Crease, Richard, TD, Professor of pathology, London
50. Currie, Mr John, Consultant surgeon, London
51. Crosfill, Mr Martin, Consultant surgeon, Penzance
52. Dall, Dr John, OBE, Consultant geriatric physician, Glasgow
53. Davenport, Dr Harold T., Consultant anaesthetist, Canada
54. Davidson, Prof Lindsay, Prof of Medicine, Birmingham
55. Davidson, Mr L., Consultant surgeon, Aberdeen
56. Davie, Dr R.D.M., (Callum) Consultant anaesthetist, Perth/BOE
57. Davies, Dr D.M., Consultant in Anaesthesia and Intensive care, London
58. Dennis, Dr Peter, General practitioner, Argyllshire
59. Dixon, Dr Alan St J., OBE, General practitioner (?) Cornwall. BRCS
60. Donald, Dr John R. TD, Neurosurgical anaesthetist, Glasgow
61. Dorward, Dr Morrison, General practitioner, Dundee
62. Drury, Professor Sir Michael, PPRCGP, Worcester
63. El-Katsha, Erian Wilson, Egyptian ANIC, anaesthetist Worksop
64. Elliott, Dr Arnold, OBE, General practitioner, London

55. Evans, Dr David W., General practitioner, Cambridge
56. Evans, Dr Glyn, General practitioner, Prestatyn, Clwyd
57. Evans, Dr Larry, General practitioner, Sydney
58. Fairlie, Dr E.J., Consultant obstetrician, York, South Africa
59. Fletcher, Dr Ron, Consultant physician, Birmingham
70. Forster, Dr David M.C., Consultant obstetrician, Essex
71. Forwell, Dr George, OBE, Medical administrator, Glasgow
72. Frame, Dr John, Lecturer, anatomy and pathology, St Andrews
73. Franklin, Dr Jeremy, General practitioner, London
74. Gaffikin, Dr Peter, Industrial Medicine, Winchester
75. Gardner, Professor Dugald, RCS Edinburgh
76. Gibson, Mr J.M.C., Consultant orthopaedic surgeon, Aberdeen
77. Graham, Mr Andrew (Andy) Consultant urologist, Glasgow
78. Gibbs, Mrs Rachel, Oxford. w/o Denis Gibbs, (RAF) London
79. Gode, Dr John D., Consultant Rheumatologist, York
80. Griffiths, Mr Harry, CBE, TD, Consultant orthopaedic surgeon, Bristol
81. Gunn, Mr A. (Tony) Consultant surgeon, Edinburgh
82. Gwilym, Major Vince, (TA) NS RAMC soldier
83. Hacking, Dr Peter, Consultant radiologist, Oxford
84. Harrow, Dr Alexander, General practitioner, Worksop
85. Heber, Dr John, Consultant anaesthetist, Redhill
86. Henderson, Dr Jimmy, Prof pathology, NY and West Indies
87. Henderson, Dr P.A., General practitioner, Corsham, Wiltshire
88. Howard, Prof John M., former USMC, Ohio, USA
89. Hughes, Dr Carl, former USMC, Maryland, USA
90. Hunt, Dr Charles W.J., General practitioner, London
91. Hutchison, Mr Archie, Consultant urologist, Glasgow
92. Howarth, Dr Nick, Consultant pathologist, Cumbria
93. Hunter, Dr Graham, General practitioner, Bexhill-on-Sea
94. Irvine, Mr Robert, Consultant surgeon, Glasgow
95. Jackson, Sir Barry, PRCS England, London
96. James, Dr Ivor, General practitioner, London
97. Kirkup, Mr John, Consultant orthopaedic surgeon, Bath
98. Kirkup, Mrs Pierrette, Bath
99. Lamont, Dr Stewart, Consultant anaesthetist, Hobart, Australia
100. Lancaster, Dr Garth, General practitioner, Market Harborough

101. Lawson, Dr J.I.M., Consultant anaesthetist, Dundee
102. Leadley, Dr J. Martin, General practitioner, Norwich
103. Leete, Mr Alec Senior, Laboratory technician, Welwyn Garden City
104. Lester, Dr John P., General practitioner, West Midlands
105. Levy, Dr Fred, General practitioner, Liverpool
106. Litton, Mr Adrian, Consultant surgeon, Southern General, Glasgow
107. Livingstone, Dr Jeremy, Consultant obstetrician, Edinburgh
108. Lloyd, A. Llewellyn, OBE, KStJ, Treasury Medical officer, Birmingham
109. Lloyd, Dr David B., General practitioner, Bath
110. Lodge, Dr J.S.H., General practitioner, Wetherby, Yorkshire
111. Lutton, Dr C.C., General practitioner, Edinburgh
112. Lyons, Mr Edward, Consultant ophthalmologist, Llandudno
113. Macdonald, Dr A. Cameron, Consultant physician, Glasgow
114. McEwen, Charles G., Consultant Ophthalmologist, Glasgow
115. Macgregor, Dr James, OBE, former CMS; PMO, Solomon Islands
116. Mackay, Dr Eric, General practitioner, Lenzie
117. MeKelvie, Mr George, OBE, Consultant urologist, Stirling
118. McKenzie, Dr K.T.C., General practitioner, Solihull
119. Macintyre, Prof Neil, Professor of Medicine, London
120. Macphie, Major General Duncan, L/RAMC, Glasgow. (NS-Regular)
121. Mann, Dr C.J.H., OBE, TD, Social Medicine, Aberdeen
122. Masson, Dr Alastair, Consultant anaesthetist, Edinburgh
123. Matheson, General John, Postgraduate Dean, Edinburgh
124. Meldrum, Dr J.A.K., Consultant anaesthetist, Birmingham
125. Merry, Dr Peter, Consultant Physical Medicine, Burnley
126. Mills, Mr Ken, Consultant orthopaedic surgeon, Aberdeen
127. Millar, Dr David, Consultant Obstetrician, Sheffield
128. Miller, Mr Roy, Consultant ENT surgeon, Lanarkshire
129. Munro, Dr John, Consultant anaesthetist, Sick Children's Glasgow
130. Myles, Mr John, Consultant orthopaedic surgeon, Hull
131. Nelson, Lt-Col R.E., QM, Swansea